PRAISE FOR FINDEPENDENCE DAY

"A financial Pilgrim's Progress which offers both entertainment and real life examples and explanations about the things a family should know to navigate the complexities of our financial system. The result is one of the few 'how-to' books you'll have trouble putting down. This book will keep you entertained and help you become rich at the same time." —*Bob Veres, Editor, Inside Information*

■ ■ ■

"I had sworn never to read another book like David Chilton's witty and wise *The Wealthy Barber*. I'd had the inspiration; it was time for more information. There's also an aggravating sameness to the twig of literature known as the personal finance novel. So I was pleasantly surprised when my friendly counterpart, Jonathan Chevreau, had me hissing, cringing and wiping tears over the characters and moral quandaries faced by his protagonist, Jamie Morelli, on his steep path to financial freedom and personal happiness. Through Morelli, Chevreau recalls way too much about the music of my youth; but I couldn't agree more with the financial advice, the strategies and caution he weaves into an engaging story. I hope he finds many readers!" —*James Daw, CFP, Toronto Star.*

■ ■ ■

"Finally, a common sense, no-hype finance book that guides you through all of life's events through the spell-binding and wonderfully written tale of Jamie and Sheena. This is a book that once you start reading you won't want to put down, and when you finish you'll emerge finance savvy and more confident about who to trust with your money." —*Linda Leatherdale, Money Editor, Toronto Sun and author, Money Is A Girl's Best Friend*

■ ■ ■

"A lifetime of common-sense money lessons packed into a highly readable novel that follows the follies and fortunes of a young couple over 20 years as they struggle to achieve financial independence." —*Gordon Pape, author, Sleep-Easy Investing*

■ ■ ■

"A financial voyage through the human lifecycle, introducing the reader to important concepts in portfolio theory, investment analysis and retirement planning. The book does a wonderful job of blending compelling fiction and financial facts and thus inspires the reader to personalize and define their own Findependence Day." —*Moshe A. Milevsky, Ph.D., Schulich School of Business, York University*

"What makes the book different are the concepts of Findependence Day and Guerilla Frugality. Every Canadian needs to think about those concepts." —*Dan Richards, Strategic Imperatives*

■ ■ ■

"Chevreau has a real winner. A good story, a wonderful morality tale and loads of financial wisdom all wrapped up in a fun read. You won't want to put it down." —*Larry Swedroe, author of Wise Investing Made Simple*

■ ■ ■

"Written without an axe to grind and sheds light on an important distinction that most people overlook – the difference between financial independence and retirement." —*Jason Heath, fee-only planner, EES Financial*

■ ■ ■

"Chevreau has crafted a tale that explains how markets and the financial industry works in a way that you don't even realize you are learning. Through casual conversations among ordinary people and the inclusion of familiar classic-rock lyrics, he has reached a new milestone of clarity in financial education." —*Mark T. Hebner, president of Index Funds Advisors and author of Index Funds: The 12-Step Program for Active Investors, 2007*

■ ■ ■

"Jonathan Chevreau's wonderful new book works on so many levels: at its core is an absorbing, realistic story that teaches us how to perform that financial balancing act that allows us to reach our dreams and goals. It reads like a terrific novel that has extra value — struggling with money is not exactly a day at the beach, but this is the closest you'll ever come to a great beach book that will help you make enough money to retire!" —*Diane McCurdy, author of the bestselling How Much Is Enough? and president of McCurdy Financial Planning*

■ ■ ■

"A fiction gem from an icon of financial journalism." —*Les Kotzer, co-author of The Family Fight*

FINDEPENDENCE DAY

One Couple's Turbulent Journey to Financial Independence

Jonathan Chevreau

First published in 2008 by

 The
Trafalgar
Group

Power Publishers Inc.
A member of the Trafalgar Group of Companies
With offices at:
280 Jarvis Street,
Toronto, Ontario
Canada M5B 2C5
www.powerpublishersinc.com

ISBN: 978-0-9811104-0-0

Library and Archives Canada Cataloguing in Publication Data

Chevreau, Jonathan, 1953-
    Findependence Day: One couple's turbulent journey to financial independence

ISBN 978-0-98111040-0-0

1. Financial planning—North America   2. Financial independence—North America

---

Text layout: Kim Monteforte, WeMakeBooks.ca
Cover art: Stuart Inglis, Pilot PMR

Printed in Canada

WITH A LITTLE HELP FROM MY FRIENDS

While all characters in this novel are fictional, Theo is a composite of many excellent financial advisors, some of whom contributed to or checked the manuscript. They include the following multi-credentialed certified financial planners:

Fred Kirby, Dimensionalplanning.ca, Armstrong, B.C.
Terry McCullough, George Brown College, Toronto.
Diane McCurdy, McCurdy Financial Planning Inc., Vancouver. B.C.
John DeGoey, Burgeonvest Securities Ltd., Toronto.
Jason Heath, EES Financial Services Ltd., Markham.

Ron Cirotto, developer of Amortization.com, helped develop some of the mortgage paydown examples.

Thanks too to Barry Fish of Fish & Associates (co-author of *The Family Fight*) and John Legge of Legge & Legge, for clarifying legal points in this manuscript.

Dan Richards, Tony Humble and the Financial Planning Standards Council also provided key input.

Finally, a word of thanks to my unofficial editor—my wife Ruth Snowden—and my official editor, Bruce McDougall. And to our teenaged daughter Helen, who graciously agreed to travel to Europe during the late stages of the manuscript.

TABLE OF CONTENTS

Foreword   ix

CHAPTER 1   **Take It to the Limit**   1
Credit cards and other bad debt

CHAPTER 2   **Money Money Money (It's a Rich Man's World)**   7
The best investment is paying off debt

CHAPTER 3   **Poor Boy Blues**   15
You can't save by spending; be an owner, not a loaner

CHAPTER 4   **Baby You're a Rich Man**   21
The concept of human capital

CHAPTER 5   **You Can't Always Get What You Want**   33
A paid-for home is the cornerstone of financial independence;
paying down mortgages

CHAPTER 6   **Teach Your Children**   45
Education plans

CHAPTER 7   **Our House**   53
Buy term life insurance and invest the difference

CHAPTER 8   **Could It Happen to Me?**   65
Disability and other types of insurance; estate planning

CHAPTER 9   **A Question of Balance**   77
Roth plans and tax free savings accounts

CHAPTER 10   **When I'm 64**   87
Government pensions

CHAPTER 11   **Taxman**   99
The leaky bucket: non-registered investment plans

CHAPTER 12   **Crash, Boom, Bang**   115
Conservative leverage and hedging stock market risk

CHAPTER 13   **Dedicated to the One I Love**   125
Asset dedication vs. asset allocation; retirement risk zone

CHAPTER 14   **It's Over**   137
Real estate; indexing

CHAPTER 15   **May Be a Price to Pay** 147
The nature of financial independence

CHAPTER 16   **Time Is On My Side** 157
Longevity insurance and annuities; leaving a legacy

CHAPTER 17   **Takin' Care of Business** 167
Multiple streams of income

CHAPTER 18   **Rehearsals for Retirement** 175
Slow and steady wins the race

Epilogue: Grow Old With Me 185
Appendix: A Peek into Theo's Library 187
About the Author 188

Foreword

Patricia Lovett-Reid

Senior Vice President, TD Waterhouse Canada,
Host of BBN's MoneyTalk

Move over Wealthy Barber, there's a new fictional financial guru in town. Jon Chevreau has coined a new term—"Findependence Day," a contraction of Financial Independence Day.

While fictional in nature it's firmly rooted in financial reality. This book is loaded with solid, practical financial advice. Chevreau makes financial planning fun, engaging and enlightening. It's a must read for anyone wanting to take control of their financial situation.

In fact, I liked this book so much it's going in the children's stockings this Christmas: all four of them, guerrilla frugality be damned.

I've known Jon for some time but had only read his non-fiction books like The Wealthy Boomer and his columns in the newspaper. But fiction? Who knew? I knew something was up when in an e-mail exchange late in the summer he told me he'd temporarily curtailed his obsession with Internet Bridge. My parents are hooked on the same game so I knew whatever had displaced it had to be serious.

But a novel? He told me it would be too boring to write another non-fiction book: too much like his day job, I think he said. He confessed to having written a "practice novel" a few years back and thought the classic novel structure was a good way to present the ups and downs of financial planning. I've read my share of Ludlums and Grishams in my time and know it's all about building suspense by having a failure or setback in every scene.

Findependence Day is not a thriller in the classic sense but you do get caught up in wondering whether the protagonists, Jamie and Sheena, will achieve their ambitious goal of financial freedom within the stated time frame. Over a 22-year span, they go through the kinds of tribulations and financial setbacks most married couples experience.

In fact, I see at least one other reviewer has likened Findependence Day to "a financial Pilgrim's Progress." That's not a bad way to sum it up. It's a fun and engaging story. Even though I've been in the financial industry for a long, long time, I've never really focused on this novel concept of Financial Independence Day. I guess the closest thing is Freedom 55. Come to think of it, Findependence 50 does have a nice ring to it!

After the financial meltdown of 2008, frugality is going to be the new reality so I think we'll be hearing plenty more about guerrilla frugality and froogers. In the book, the common-sense approach to frugality, savings and investments is promulgated not by one but two certified financial planners: the wise old Theo and the vinyl-loving hippie, Bernie.

People have a financial age and a chronological age. Rarely are the two the same—you can demonstrate it's never too late to start saving and investing but the sooner you take control of your financial situation the better.

When you enter into a relationship you are in it emotionally and financially. Work through the issues, confront the facts, be honest and you stand a better chance of not becoming a divorce statistic.

I'm not going to give away the plot but Findependence Day is also a love story. I think couples will learn a lot about both money and their relationship by reading this book. Love and money are more intertwined in the lives of modern couples than most realize.

Since the book closes with a reference to a John Lennon song, I'll close this foreword with another Beatles quote that didn't make it into the book: "Your love gives me a thrill but your loving don't pay my bills."

Patricia's best-selling personal finance books include Live Well, Retire Well; Surprise! You're Wealthy; Get Real; and Retirement Strategies for Women.

Chapter 1

Take It to the Limit

[EAGLES, 1975]

A mong the myriad minor stars inhabiting the reality television galaxy, Didi Quinlan had an unusual specialty: her popular weekly network television show featured young couples starting their married lives mired in debt.

Based in the Windy City, the producers of *Debt March* had no difficulty finding takers happy to expose themselves to millions of financial voyeurs. Guests who implemented Didi's suggestions about frugality expected to be given a few thousand dollars to help pay off their credit-card debt. But the real pay-off, no matter how humiliating, was the requisite 15 minutes of fame.

Waiting on the set for the show to begin, Jamie and Sheena Morelli were typical fodder for *Debt March*. They were both 28, broke and willing to display their financial ineptitude to a nation-wide audience.

Jamie squared his shoulders and ran his fingers through his thick brown curls. He knew he could handle Quinlan: he dealt with worse every day at his sales job at Tech Heaven, a giant electronics chain, where he talked gadget-hungry consumers into upgrading their toys. Most of them were like Sheena, who couldn't visit a shopping mall without adding $100 to mounting piles of credit-card debt. As a schoolteacher, Sheena could hold her own with pre-teens but Didi Quinlan was a different story.

Jamie knew Didi was a flamboyant personality who loved to torment her guests with her devastating wit. Her handlers tended to slap on a little too much makeup for the cameras, heavy on the mascara and bronzer. In person, she looked younger and less sophisticated than the camera revealed.

Jamie's thoughts were interrupted by a technician, who put a microphone on his lapel, handed Sheena a glass of water and scurried off the set. The red light on one of the camera robots came alive. As the familiar *Debt March* theme played on the monitors, Didi settled confidently in the host's chair.

"Welcome viewers, debtors and creditors. Today our guests are Giamo and Sheena Morelli, a childless working couple who live in a rented urban condo north of the border. Thanks for flying down to join us."

"Thank you," Jamie said, "but please, everyone calls me Jamie, except my mother." Giamo was the name his hard-working Italian parents had given him a few years after they immigrated to Upper New York State. He was Jamie all through high school and he was Jamie when he met the love of his life, the green-eyed red head named Sheena.

"I'm certainly not your mama," Didi said with a grimace, triggering a ripple of laughter from the audience, "So Jamie and Sheena, how much money do you owe?"

Jamie glanced at Sheena, uncertain if he should start first. As he hesitated, the TV monitors zeroed in on her face.

"I have $20,000 left on my student loans," Sheena said.

"You're a college grad?" Didi smiled.

"I studied English and history but—" Sheena said.

"Let me guess, you didn't minor in accounting or personal finance," Didi interrupted. She spun her chair to look directly at Jamie.

"How about you, Jamie? How much do you owe on student loans?"

"I worked part-time while studying at the electronics institute so I didn't have to borrow."

"How about credit cards?"

"We owe $12,000 on credit cards plus $10,000 in car loans," Sheena said.

"Which cards?"

"The big ones. You'd know them by heart," Jamie quipped, "Plus a few department store cards."

"They're the worst because they charge the most interest," Didi said, "Get rid of them, then tackle the regular credit cards." Didi gave Sheena a sympathetic smile but when the camera zoomed in on Didi, Jamie sensed something was amiss.

"Sheena, do you have these cards with you? Our viewers may like to see them."

"Sure." Sheena picked out a few from her wallet and waved two well-known bank credit cards before the camera.

"I love these cards. I couldn't tell you how many scrapes they got me out of. These two I got in college when I really needed credit. So today, we use them first. We pay off the minimum balance every month too!"

"The credit-card companies love people like you," Didi deadpanned.

That went over Sheena's head. "I guess we have a great credit rating. Some of these we didn't even have to apply for," Sheena said proudly.

Out of the corner of his eye, Jamie could see Didi reach for something shiny: the bright TV lights were reflecting off it into his field of vision.

The camera zeroed in on the pair of scissors Didi was brandishing. She made a cutting motion, "It's time, kids. Will you cut them up or shall I?"

Jamie and Sheena exchanged surprised glances. "I can," Sheena said, reaching for the scissors. When she cut two department store cards in half, Didi looked triumphant. But Sheena seemed more doubtful as she got to the cards she relied on every day. As the scissors drew nearer to her shiny new bankcard, she stopped. Jamie saw the hesitation in her face and knew tears were close to the surface.

"I can't do this," Sheena cried in anguish, placing the scissors and cards down on the table, next to her untouched water glass, "These cards have always been there for me when I really needed them."

Jamie turned to encourage his young wife with a quick hug. This earned him only a stricken glance. Then the dam broke and tears coursed down her cheeks.

Didi didn't miss a beat, raising her hands in mock frustration.

"Credit cards are an issue for you two. You're a nice fellow but you and the Missus have a problem. You can't ascend the tower of wealth while mired in debt in the basement."

Jamie's face reddened.

Didi flashed a motherly smile: "Stop spending and start saving. Let me drill two words into your skulls: *guerrilla frugality*. Say it for me."

"Guerrilla frugality," Jamie parroted, sheepishly.

Didi addressed the audience. "Jamie and Sheena have the same problem as you. You earn too little and spend too much. You run out of money before you run out of month. Am I right or am I right?"

Sporadic applause.

"Jamie, you buy coffee or snacks at work?"

"Sure."

"Say you go twice a day or buy your lunch. $10 a day is nothing, you think? That's $50 a week or $2,500 a year you could save without breaking a sweat."

Jamie nodded.

"You smoke?"

"Used to. Sheena still has the odd one." The camera moved to Sheena for a moment, just as she was dabbing her eyes with a Kleenex. She looked miserable. Jamie didn't expect she'd volunteer to speak again on the segment.

"How much?" Didi probed, "Two packs a day?"

"For awhile."

"Know how much you squandered? Say you spend $10 a day on the habit. Multiply by 365 gets you $3,650 a year. Multiply by 40 years and it's almost $150,000." She pretended to inhale an imaginary cigarette and exhale a cloud of smoke. "A fortune up in smoke!"

"We could almost buy our condo for that," Jamie smiled, "That's why I stopped— that and my health of course!"

Didi lit into Jamie as if he were a truant schoolboy.

"Do you know how many viewers whine about having no money, then light up another one? Let me tell you, Mister, we're talking about much more than $150,000. Compounded at 6% in tax-sheltered investments, that habit alone could cost $600,000 over your lifetime. More than a million with a 9% return."

"You're preaching to the converted, Didi." Jamie thought of his brother in Rochester still wasting $5 a day on his butts.

Didi pointed to the audience.

"But THEY are not converted. THEY keep buying lottery tickets, booze, junk food, candy, cigarettes and waste a small fortune." She shook her fist, "Then they complain they're too poor to pay off their credit cards."

She challenged the camera as the operator zoomed in on her.

"PEOPLE. Wake up. It's time for guerrilla frugality. Budget. Keep track of expenses. Spend less than you earn. You've got to be *frugal*." She drew out the word frugal, using her best fake Scottish accent.

Jamie stared, speechless, as Didi turned back to him.

"Thank you for receiving my tough love, Jamie and Sheena. Next we have a fee-only financial advisor who's going to give our guests some free financial planning tips," Didi said, "Please welcome Theodoris Konstantin."

Konstantin was a tanned, elegant man who looked to be in his early 50s. Jamie figured he was one of those aging wealthy boomers who were retired or just about.

"Always a pleasure," Konstantin said.

"Theo," Didi began, obviously well acquainted with her guest, "What do you think of our young guests' financial situation?"

Theo gave Sheena a reassuring smile.

"They're typical of many young couples who succumb to the lure of easy credit and instant gratification. I don't see many in my practice because my wealthy clients are older and have no debt. I—"

Didi cut him off. "Is there any hope for Jamie and Sheena, Theo? Do they need electro shock therapy? What can we do to wake them up?" As she said the word 'shock' she looked at Jamie as if she were willing to administer such a shock herself.

"There's always hope, Didi. Time is on their side. First, they must eliminate all credit-card debt and other consumer loans. Then they should buy a house and pay it off as soon as possible. The foundation of financial independence is a paid-for home."

"Seems to me if they want to plunge into home ownership they would be perfect candidates for a 35- or 40-year amortization schedule," Didi responded, "It wouldn't cost much more than what they're wasting on rent right now. How much do you throw away renting your condo, Jamie?"

"$1,400 a month," he stammered.

Theo frowned at Didi's question, though the camera was still on her. Now it zoomed out to show all four of them in a single shot.

"The bank said we'd qualify for the 35-year schedule."

"Sure," Theo replied, "You qualify if you can fog a mirror. If anyone takes the whole 35 years to pay off a home, that would be a costly financial mistake. The monthly payments seem low and you can buy more house, but you'll pay so much interest in the first 20 years of the schedule the house will end up costing you three times its purchase price."

Jamie whistled and was startled when the microphones picked it up.

It was Didi's turn to frown. "But they don't have to take 35 years to pay it off. The point is to stop renting and at least get them into a home of their own."

Theo looked bemused. "As long as they're disciplined enough to take advantage of the prepayment and payment increase privileges, they could soon get back onto a 25-year amortization schedule or—better yet—a shorter one still."

Didi smiled. "Then they're in the game."

"True. The problem comes if they spend the extra cash flow on consumption and 'never get round' to paying down principal. Better to start small with a house they can afford in a reasonable part of town. Pay it off as fast as possible: ten or 15 years, not 30 or 35. Once mortgage-free they can move up to a bigger home in a better district, remortgaging if necessary."

"When did you retire, Theo?" Didi asked.

"I don't consider myself retired. However, I reached financial independence when I was 52, two years ago. That's when the income from my investments and all other sources first exceeded my income from full-time employment. I didn't *have* to work for the man any more."

"So you retired at 52?"

"I didn't say that. The day after achieving Financial Independence you may be doing exactly the same thing you were doing the day before. The difference is you're doing the work because you *want* to do it, not because you perceive you must."

"You're a smart investor, Theo," Didi said, "Any tips on how Jamie and Sheena could invest in the stock market?"

As the camera focused on Theo, Jamie thought he looked like a wise and kindly professor. But Theo shook his head at Didi's question: "Young people should forget about investing until they've eliminated their debts. Enrol in the company pension plan if it's offered but no investment pays as well as eliminating high-interest debt."

"Sounds like a plan," Didi deadpanned.

Theo smiled. "You took the words out of my mouth. They need a financial plan to map out the next 20 to 30 years. Jamie, you could start by declaring right now on TV when your Findependence Day will be."

"Findependence Day?" Didi said, raising her eyebrows. It seemed this was a new term even for Didi.

"Financial Independence Day or Findependence Day for short. And in French 'fin dépendance' would mean the 'end of dependence.'"

Didi didn't cut in so Theo continued: "The day I set mine, I couldn't fit all the words 'Financial Independence Day' onto that little square on the calendar, so I crossed it off and shortened it. It's been 'Findependence Day' ever since. Tiny calendar, big plans!"

With that, Theo threw his well-manicured hands open and pushed them forward, upward and outward, as if releasing a messenger bird to a yearning throng. "Jamie, you should circle a date on the calendar. Pick some day in the future, like a birthday, when you believe you should achieve Financial Independence. That's your Findependence Day. In my case, I chose June 1st of the year my youngest son graduated from university. I would still be only 52, enjoying my best years."

"Did you make it?" Didi asked.

"On the nose," said Theo, "There's great power in drawing a line in the sand and saying this is the day. If you fall behind, take steps to speed it up. If you think you'll overshoot, you can take a few more days of vacation."

"So," Didi said, pushing Jamie, "Can you declare when *your* Findependence Day will be?"

Jamie paused, knowing the cameras were picking up on his discomfort. "When my parents immigrated to the United States, they achieved financial independence through hard work and… "—here he glanced at Didi—"guerrilla frugality."

Didi laughed, pleased he'd picked up on her pet phrase. "So when, Jamie?"

Flustered, Jamie said, "I don't know. Dad died before he could enjoy his financial independence. I want it to be while I'm still young enough to enjoy life. I'll let you know when I decide on the day."

"Deal," Didi said, shaking hands with her guests, "We'll have to get you back on the show some day."

She turned again to the audience with her trademark smirking smile, as the technicians rolled the credits to close the segment.

Chapter 2

Money Money Money (It's a Rich Man's World)

[ABBA, 1976]

J amie and Sheena returned to the green room where guests awaited their moment of glory. They'd parked their carry-on luggage there and Sheena needed to compose herself and repair the damage to her makeup. A TV monitor was running *Flip This Mansion*, the reality show that followed *Debt March*.

Jamie grabbed the remote on the table and muted it. "Hey Babe," Jamie tried the upbeat approach, "At least we're famous."

"Famous for being financial cretins," Sheena said, her eyes still red from recent tears, "I've never been so humiliated in my life."

Jamie handed her a tissue, attempting empathy.

"Honey, it's not as if you didn't know this could happen. Didi is famous for her card-cutting shtick. Did you really think she was going to let you off the hook?"

"Of course not," Sheena sniffed, "When I got to the bank card, I started thinking 'What if we need this?' It's our lifeline. You know how it is with us: we're one paycheque from the poorhouse. One unexpected emergency and poof!"

Jamie's tone changed to one of concern. "I don't like it any more than you do, hon. We just have to start being more like Mum and Dad."

Sheena snapped out of her reflective mood, her green eyes blazing. "I don't need another Horatio Alger tale of how frugal, hard-working Italians found the Promised Land. They just made a lucky call when they opened the diner."

"Maybe," Jamie's voice was barely audible, "But they knew about saving for a rainy day. They were practising guerrilla frugality when Didi Quinlan was still in diapers."

Sheena got up from the couch, nervously twisting her wedding ring. She turned and looked at her handsome husband.

"Life was simpler for your parents. There were no cell phones or satellite TV or iPods or any of that junk you sell at Tech Heaven. We spend more every month on cable TV and Internet access than Giancarlo and Fabiana used to pay in rent."

"They didn't pay it for long," Jamie retorted, "After two years working round the clock, they'd saved up a down payment for the building that housed the diner. We had a great childhood living in the apartment above it."

Jamie paused, lost in memories. "Victor and I worked long hours in the diner, after school and weekends. We did everything from cooking to serving tables to mopping floors."

"It must have been a wonderful experience."

"We didn't stay there forever. I remember the day we moved to a house. It was an 18-foot wide semi with a tiny back yard. I was eleven and ecstatic about moving to a real house."

"If you want to call it a house," Sheena said, defiant, "A dumpy little semi in the wrong part of town. Look how little it took back then for a down payment … A few thousand dollars. They lucked out. Try that today."

"They had the right idea. I'll tell you this: we're turning our financial lives around, starting now. I'm never going to be publicly humiliated like this again."

It was Sheena's turn to play the role of the sympathetic spouse. "Maybe we could get a line of credit?"

"We could do that to consolidate our loans at a lower interest rate. But that's just a band-aid solution. Didi's right about guerrilla frugality. It's a war out there and we have to spend less than we earn. We can't count on us both earning regular paycheques forever."

Sheena leaned closer. "What are you saying?"

"If the economy goes in the toilet either of us could lose our job overnight. Then we couldn't even make the minimum payments on the cards, which is how we got in this mess in the first place."

Jamie paused, as a commercial break on the TV ended and *Flip This Mansion* resumed. The camera panned across a 10,000-square-foot palace with a lawn that looked better groomed than the average putting green.

"Look at the people living in those McMansions," he said, gesturing at the TV. "You think they have an emergency cash cushion they could live on for six months? Six days is more like it. Didi is bang on about eliminating credit card debt and building up an emergency fund."

A producer popped her head into the room, "Did you want a copy of the show? We can courier a DVD to your home."

Jamie paused before responding: "No thanks. We don't need to be reminded how we made idiots of ourselves on nation-wide television. But you can tell Didi I've decided."

"On what, sir?" the young girl said, evidently an assistant to someone higher up the broadcasting food chain.

"I've decided on my Findependence Day."

"Your what?"

"Don't you watch your own show?" Jamie said, trying to be patient, "Financial Independence Day. Tell Didi my Findependence Day will be July 4, the day I turn 50."

"I'll tell her that, sir," the girl said, and scurried out as quickly as she had arrived.

"The day you turn 50?" Sheena had recovered her composure. "That's just 22 years from now."

"I like round numbers," Jamie grinned, "Now all we have to do is find someone to help us get there."

■ ■ ■

Holding hands, Jamie and Sheena left the green room of the TV station and walked slowly to the bank of elevators. Jamie would have taken the stairs but knew there was no way Sheena would do that for 20 flights, even if it were down.

As he pressed the "lobby" button, a well-tanned manicured hand appeared between the doors. Jamie recognized Theo, the financial advisor from the show, and punched the button to reopen the door. Theo was chatting with a producer as they stepped into the elevator.

"…No, I don't think he even knew the meaning of the word diversification," was all Jamie could catch of the end of that conversation.

With a barely perceptible nod, Theo thanked Jamie for holding the door open. He was carrying a laptop computer slung over his shoulder and a piece of wheeled luggage. He glanced at Sheena. "All cried out now? You certainly made an impression."

Sheena blushed, as Jamie put his arm protectively around his petite wife.

"Don't take it to heart," Theo said, "Didi can be vicious when it comes to young couples in debt. She believes tough love is the kindest approach in the long run."

"I'm okay," Sheena said, despite her reddened eyes.

"I like your idea of Findependence Day," Jamie interjected. He glanced at the elevator console and realized they were already half way down.

"Say," Jamie's tone of voice changed, "Do you think you could do our financial plan and become our advisor? I've decided on my Financial Independence Day."

"Already? You had no idea when Didi asked."

"I do now," Jamie said with certainty, "It's the day I turn 50."

"Findependence 50," Theo replied, "Ambitious target."

"I want to be financially independent and follow my dreams while I'm young enough to remember them."

"Who doesn't?"

"When can we meet? We'd pay you."

"I don't take credit cards," Theo smiled, then added: "I'm not taking on new clients. I'm financially independent myself now and have strict criteria as to what new clients I take on."

The elevator had reached the ground floor. Theo let Sheena and the producer exit first, then motioned to Jamie.

"Unfortunately," Theo seemed apologetic; "I don't take on clients until they have eliminated all debts. Come see me in a few years."

Theo said his goodbyes to the producer and began walking across a massive lobby filled with light from the three-story windows. Jamie kept pace as Theo neared the exit.

Theo stood aside briefly to let two well-dressed executives pass through the revolving doors. He smiled apologetically and explained, "I have a plane to catch."

"Which flight you on?" Jamie asked.

Theo was taken aback by this but answered "7 pm to Pearson." He looked at his watch anxiously.

"Same here but we're on the 8 pm flight. Why don't we share a cab to the airport?" Jamie said.

Theo hesitated and Jamie continued with a smile, "Guerrilla frugality."

Theo laughed. "Very well, if you put it that way."

Outside, Theo tried to hail a cab but had no luck. Jamie put his fingers in his mouth and let loose a shrill wolf whistle. It caught the attention of a cabbie on the other side of the street, who pulled a U-Turn and picked them up.

The driver's eyes met Theo's and he said simply "O'Hare."

As the cabbie put Theo's luggage in the trunk, Theo asked Jamie if he and Sheena had any luggage.

"Just these carry-on bags," Jamie said, lifting his own from his shoulder and indicating Sheena's. "We travel light."

"We just flew in this morning for Didi's show," Sheena said, "We couldn't afford to stay overnight."

Theo held the door for Sheena while Jamie got in the other side. "I stayed at the Drake last night, but I had a few other appointments," Theo said.

"You have clients in Chicago?" Sheena said.

"A few. Some of the couples here began as cross-border romances like yourselves. How did you two meet?"

Jamie glanced at the driver's face and his ID card and satisfied himself they matched. Then he squeezed Sheena's hand and leaned across his bride to face Theo. "Sheena came down to Rochester to watch her brother Eamon play soccer against me. She swept me off my feet. A year later we married and I transferred to a Tech Heaven franchise in Mississauga. How would you like a couple of new clients from there?"

Theo flashed a sympathetic smile. "I don't take on clients with no financial assets and who are still in debt. I may make exceptions for those who have cut their mortgage principal in half. But no credit card debt."

"I thought all financial advisors are looking for new clients."

Theo turned to face Jamie, amused.

"There was a time when I would have been thrilled to take on a couple as distinguished as you and Sheena," Theo said, "Like many in my business, I started as a commission-based stock broker. Then, midway through my career, I sold rear-load mutual funds." He sighed wistfully, "If only I knew you then."

"Why not now?" Sheena asked.

"At this stage in your lives, even if you eliminated your debts, your first investments would probably be mutual funds. But I've gone beyond those and so have most of my clients."

"There's something better than mutual funds?" Jamie looked surprised.

"At your stage in life, there are great advantages to mutual funds. They give you professional security selection, are broadly diversified and you can keep adding to them in small monthly amounts. I'd suggest you take that approach with equity mutual funds as soon as you are debt-free."

"Equity funds. That's the stock market, right?" interjected Sheena.

"Correct," Theo said. "But my clients have at least $250,000 invested. They may have some in funds but tend to invest in alternative forms of managed money or in stocks directly."

"$250,000?" Jamie looked pained, "That's a lot."

"It seems so in your 20s," Theo said, "At that age I thought even $25,000 was a king's ransom. But if you're talking about age 50 as your Findependence Day, you'd better get used to numbers like that."

The cabbie ran his second late yellow light in a row. Theo frowned.

"If you don't get paid commissions, how are you paid?"

"For a long time, I charged those clients a fee of 1% of their assets a year."

"On $250,000 that's $2,500 a year."

"Right," Theo said, "It seems a lot but some of it is tax-deductible. My clients are as worried about taxes as they are about fees. Wealthier clients pay less than 1%. They believe the fees pay for themselves if the advisor stops them from making disastrous financial decisions."

"You said you were once fee-based?" Jamie said, with one eye on the speedometer. He checked to make sure Sheena's seatbelt was tightened.

"Yes, all the time it took me to reach my own financial independence I used a fee-based approach, or more accurately, an asset-based one."

"Now you're retired?" Sheena persisted.

"Financially independent," Theo corrected her. "I'm not retired. I still do everything I used to when I was a full-time advisor. At one point, I sold my entire client base to a younger advisor but after a few months of golf and bridge—"

"Bridge," Jamie grimaced. "You sound like my parents. Everyone I know plays poker."

Theo ignored this. The cab was now on open road and proceeding a good ten clicks over the speed limit. "After a few months, I missed the action and frankly some of my more personable clients. I still ran my own portfolio and watched the markets, so a few clients asked if they could pay me a small quarterly retainer so they could in effect copy my portfolio."

"Did you buy stocks and funds for them?"

"No, they do that themselves," Theo said, "I just give them guidance. I suggest they set up an account at an online discount brokerage, then implement the Lazy Portfolio."

"Lazy Portfolio?" Sheena sounded intrigued. It was the first time Jamie had ever noticed her express any interest in investing instead of spending.

"It's a combination of low-cost indexed investments, a few blue-chip dividend-paying stocks and government bonds. At my age, I don't want to follow the markets that closely any more. Not every day."

"Could you prepare a financial plan showing us how to do that?" Jamie asked.

"I could but I think you need the service that goes along with it. I have a friend in the business. I suggest you consult with him. He's also the owner of the Vinyl Cave on Lakefront Boulevard."

"Vinyl Cave?"

"It's a little shop in the west end that sells old vinyl records. He's like me: a relic from the 50s and 60s."

"You know vinyl," Sheena interjected. She always livened up when history came into the conversation. "Those old 331/3 RPM long-playing records. Eamon was the only one of us kids who wanted Dad's vinyl before he passed away. He got some great old stuff like Beatles, Beach Boys, Eagles, Strawbs…"

"We still sell the odd Sony turntable at Tech Heaven," Jamie said. "Mostly to old codgers."

"Drop by the store some time and talk to my friend Bernie. He used to be one of my clients before becoming certified as an advisor himself."

"Is he financially independent too?" Jamie asked. Looking through the cab window, he noted a sign that said O'Hare was two miles away.

"I'd say so. He owns the whole building. He lives in one apartment above the store and rents the other two."

"Like mum and dad lived over the diner. Dad planned to stop work at 60," Jamie's eyes misted up as he said this. "He was 58 when he had his heart attack. They buried him back in Bari."

Theo nodded solemnly. "On the other hand, I've known clients who died within months of retiring. Some had no real plans for how to spend their final years. They were pushed out of the corporation and knew no other life."

"No hobbies?" Jamie said. "I'd have no trouble filling up my leisure time with music, poker, golf, reading, travel, you name it. It would also be great to have more time to do volunteer work."

"Jamie helps out at local food banks," Sheena said, "and seldom misses the monthly breakfast at the Rotary Club."

"It may not be financially easy in the middle class but so many people don't even have what we have," Jamie said.

Theo nodded in approval. "You're talking about Semi-Retirement or the First Retirement. If you can give back to the community, so much the better. It's a logical progression from raising children and taking care of aging parents."

"When I'm retired I also plan to read a lot and learn a foreign language," Sheena said. In a soft voice she added, "I also dream of one day writing a novel for pre-teens."

"That's another feature of the First Retirement," Theo nodded. "It's a chance to undertake creative projects and discover talents you never knew you had. Who knows, you may even end up getting paid for your trouble."

"That would be a bonus," Jamie said.

"Some people leave big corporations but start their own small business. Like Bernie. He put in his 25 years as a broker with a big investment firm and got a nice employer pension."

"Like the great Defined Benefit pension Sheena will get."

"I noticed from the show's briefing document that Sheena is a teacher," Theo said. "Are you on permanent staff?"

Sheena nodded.

"Bernie's pension isn't inflation-indexed like yours but he's achieved his financial independence and works for the fun of it. He supplements his income and keeps his brain active. Personally, I think he enjoys talking with his customers."

The cab had arrived at O'Hare. Theo gave the cabbie a corporate Amex card, waving off Jamie's attempt to split the fare.

As the cabbie handed him his luggage, Theo looked again at his watch. "I have to hustle. Nice to meet you both. Drop in on Bernie. Quite a community congregates there."

■ ■ ■

Two weeks after *Debt March* aired the phone had stopped ringing and life was returning to normal at the high-rise condominium the Morellis rented. From the 17th floor, Jamie could see the entire west end of the city: freeways, malls, other condos and apartments: acres of concrete broken only by the odd oasis of greenery. *It's okay for now but no place to raise a family.*

From the balcony, he could just see Sheena in the tiny kitchen. She was making an effort to cook more, though she loved eating out as much as he did.

"Can I make a salad, Hon?" he yelled.

"Sure."

Sheena opened the refrigerator door to grab some ingredients and frowned at the state of the appliance. "This is way too old and small," she said, "Why can't Rob and Janice get us a new one?" At least they were on a first-name basis with their landlords, Jamie thought.

"When we buy our own condo, we can get a new set of appliances," he said. "Till then we'll make do."

"What'll we use for the down payment?"

"We only need 5% if we get a high-ratio mortgage."

"Mum can lend us that much."

Jamie stopped chopping onions for a second. From what he knew of his mother-in-law, she was in worse financial shape than her youngest daughter.

"Forget Clara. She can barely get by on her widow's pension as it is. If you stopped buying shoes and dresses for six months, we'd see our way clear soon enough."

Sheena whirled around to face him, no easy matter in the tiny alcove Rob and Janice described as a "well-fitted galley kitchen."

"If you stopped buying CDs and DVDs, we could be there in a year or two."

"At least I get a discount."

"Now you mention Clara, there's something I want to discuss. I've been thinking about this ever since Dad passed away."

"MMmm?" Jamie was only half paying attention as he tossed the salad. His father-in-law, Patrick, had been buried two years earlier.

"With one less O'Connor on the planet, wouldn't it be nice to get started on the next generation?"

That got his attention. "What are you saying?"

"It's time to get started on our own family. I'm going to be 30 soon. We can't wait forever."

"Great. One less income and one more mouth to feed."

"I'd only be off for a year. It doesn't have to be right away but time is moving on. I want a real family."

"I thought you loved your students?" That was one of the things he loved about Sheena: her dream of writing uplifting fiction for the young 'tweens' she taught every day.

"I do, but every few years I say goodbye to them forever. I want a lifelong connection to my own flesh and blood."

"We can't afford it right now, honey," Jamie's burnt-almond eyes were dark with worry. "Let's wipe out the credit card debt before we start talking about children and home ownership."

"But you heard that advisor on Didi's show. Home ownership is the foundation of Financial Independence." The mushrooms sizzled as she added them to the hot oil.

"That doesn't mean we have to fill one up with bambinos the day after tomorrow." Jamie knew he was being blunt, but it was how he felt.

As the youngest son in a large noisy Italian family, Jamie wasn't averse to the idea of children when the time was right. "Tell you what, the lease on this place expires in a few months. Let's ask Rob and Janice if they'd like to sell it to us."

Their landlords had dropped hints about this in the past. Even if the offer was no longer on, a spell of house hunting might deflect Sheena from the parenthood thing, Jamie thought. He squeezed her from behind and nibbled her ear.

He was content with his life as it was now, although it would be nice if there were less financial pressure, he thought anxiously. He liked playing poker with the guys at work, or online with complete strangers. He enjoyed playing soccer and watching the World Cup in the sports bars across the city. Most of all, he loved his gadgets, toys and music. And while he seldom revealed his full vision of his future, he still harboured dreams of becoming a full-time singer-songwriter some day.

Some day, when it's Findependence Day, he mused.

"Let's do it," Sheena interrupted his reverie. "I'll mention it to Janice when I give her the rent cheque next week."

"Sure thing, honey," he tried to look upbeat as he gave her a quick hug. This is it, he thought, the beginning of the end. Got to get serious about cutting spending. *Guerrilla frugality here we come.*

"I was thinking I'd brown-bag it to work three or four days a week," Jamie said. "Could you show me how to make a tuna fish sandwich again?"

Chapter 3

Poor Boy Blues

[BARCLAY JAMES HARVEST, 1974]

J amie's brown-bagging routine was approaching its third week. He was taking public transit every second day to get to Tech Heaven. "We're frugality guerrillas," he thought with a self-congratulatory smile.

He hadn't been sure what Didi had meant until he looked the word guerrilla up in the Oxford dictionary. It informed him that guerrilla is a noun: "a member of a small independent group taking part in irregular warfare, typically against larger regular forces."

Clearly, Didi meant the large regular forces were modern consumer society, with the giant sales, advertising, marketing and credit industries conspiring to extract every last dollar from the ordinary Joe. To combat those forces required donning the fatigues of frugality guerrillas and doing battle against the consumption leviathan.

Jamie also found himself taking his job more seriously. It was one thing to cut expenses to live within one's means but the ultimate remedy was to increase income. He received a small base salary, enough to cover basic expenses; but like most sales people, he made his big money from commissions and bonuses. He started working longer hours, nights and weekends, hoping one day to move up to management, where the hours were more mainstream.

Returning to the condo late one evening, he was surprised to find the lights off and the apartment empty. Unusual, Jamie thought, since the school day's early end usually meant Sheena beat him home and had supper ready by the time he dragged his weary carcass through the door.

He flipped on the lights in the living room and fired up the stereo. Tearing the plastic off the wrapper of a new CD he'd bought at work, he slipped it into the player, pushing the volume up about twice as high as usual. It was the latest from the Droll Trolls, a band he fancied had the same sound as his own band, were he ever actually to form one. They had the same hard-hitting lyrics he used to write when the rock-and-roll dream first seized him in high school. The sound was melodic rock, with lots of keyboards and synthesizers.

Midway through the fourth cut, Sheena bustled through the door, in better spirits than she'd been in weeks—certainly since the TV appearance. Jamie pointed the remote at the stereo—Love that sound, he thought, admiring the high-end speakers he'd installed himself—and turned down the volume. Sheepishly, he tried to hide the bright yellow bag the CD had come in.

"Haven't heard these guys before," she said. Then, mischievously: "New CD?"

Jamie squirmed and came clean, pulling the bag out from under the chair cushion. He waved it and declared, "Very perceptive, Mrs. Morelli. What brings you here at such a late hour?"

She brandished a designer bag from a high-end fashion boutique. Jamie could tell it contained at least two pairs of new shoes. Still holding the evidence of his own fall from grace, he bit his lip, refraining from making his usual Imelda Marcos crack.

Sheena pulled out a pair of royal blue pumps, slipped them on, and struck one of those poses she'd learned during a brief stint at modelling school. "Like them?" she beamed. "Fiona helped me pick them out."

"You and your sister been hitting the stores again?" he replied lightly, aware he was in no position to lecture about unnecessary purchases.

"Want to know the best thing? I saved money when I bought these."

Jamie's brow furrowed, "They were on sale?"

"50% off. That's why I bought two pairs."

"You'd have saved 100% if you hadn't bought either pair." Jamie couldn't resist delivering this mild admonition. The Trolls were playing a song he recognized from the radio: *Consumer Daze*. It seemed oddly timed considering their conversation.

"No darling," Sheena executed a half turn in front of the hall-way mirror. "I mean we saved money when I bought these shoes with…"—a pause as she reached for her purse and came up with a bright red card—"with this fantastic Spend 'n Save card I got from the new bank branch in the mall. Fiona got one too."

Now Jamie knew what she was talking about. He'd seen the Spend 'n Save commercials on the ball games. The cards seemed too good to be true. He shuddered at the thought of Sheena and her sister egging each other on at the mall.

"This is how it works," Sheena said, in the flush of enthusiasm for this new marvel of financial engineering. "Whenever I buy a coffee at, say, Starbucks, for $1.25, they round up to $2."

"So your $1.25 coffee costs $2. How does that get us to Findependence Day?" Jamie was unable to restrain the sarcasm from creeping into his voice.

"That's the beauty of it. We're not spending that extra 75 cents. It's going straight into a bank savings account!" She was practically panting. "And it pays interest! 3% a year!"

"Let me get this straight. You had $2 and the next moment you've consumed a coffee and have 75 cents left that's going to pay you interest?"

"That's it," Sheena said. "But it gets better. There's also an option where you can round up to the nearest five dollars."

"I get it. So the $1.25 coffee costs you an extra $3.75."

"No, silly. You're saving $3.75 and they're paying you interest. Real interest. Just think—if you could do that every day you'd be at your Findependence Day much faster."

"Couldn't you put the $5 directly into a high-interest savings account? Then they'd pay you interest on $5 instead of $3.75."

"Sure, but who has that kind of discipline?" Sheena said, a cloud descending on her face. "This way we get our cake and eat it too. Like the card says, we spend and we save. I love it."

Unconvinced, Jamie shook his head in disbelief as he reached for the Trolls jewel case.

"One more thing," Sheena added. Jamie stopped in mid-reach. He could tell from the tone of her voice he wasn't going to like it but his tight smile told her to continue.

"Now we're saving so much money, I thought we should celebrate by replacing the bedroom furniture."

"You didn't?" He straightened slowly, turning to face Sheena.

"It's coming next week—30% off with free delivery."

"Did you use your Spend n Save?"

"No, that's for small day-to-day purchases. Thank goodness Home Superstore sent me a new card after I destroyed the first one on TV."

"Sheena, I've told you dozens of times department store cards are the worst. They charge interest well north of 20%." Jamie could hear the hint of panic in his own voice.

"I know but we don't have to pay any interest for the next six months." Sheena's excitement dampened as she tried to explain her way out of what was not shaping up to be such a great idea.

Jamie sighed. "Then just when you've forgotten about it and the cat's peed on the furniture, bang, suddenly we're hit with a 20% interest charge. How much interest did you say the Spend 'n Save card pays us?"

"Three per cent."

"Do I have to spell it out for you, Sheena?" He kicked a shopping bag out of the way in annoyance. "Save at 3% before tax. Spend at 20% after tax? Your arithmetic makes no sense. You can't spend your way to saving. It's impossible. A marketing ploy designed to take advantage of gullible people."

"I thought you'd be pleased." She was crestfallen but Jamie ignored the tears he knew were building up. Sheena picked up the shopping bags, folding them for the recycle bin.

"Do I look pleased?" he exploded. "We're the only people who ever see the bedroom. Keep this up and we'll never get out of the hole." Jamie's frustration showed in his voice.

She pressed her lips together to stop them trembling.

"It has to stop, Sheena. If you want babies and a home, we have to stop spending more than we earn." Jamie felt the panic rise in his chest as he thought of the new furniture. If he were going to transform her into a frugality guerrilla he'd need help.

"There's someone you need to talk to."

He ignored the furious slam of the bedroom door and the sound of new shoes hitting the wall. Somehow he had to find the strength to insist that Sheena cut up the credit cards for good.

■ ■ ■

Al Peters wheeled his leased gold Lexus into the Tech Heaven parking lot late Friday afternoon a few weeks after the Morellis' appearance on *Debt March*. Thankful that red-light cameras hadn't yet been installed, he enjoyed the adrenaline rush he'd just felt from gunning the high-performance car through the last intersection.

A sophisticated big-spender, Peters could have passed for one of the British soccer players who perennially contended for the World Cup, though the discipline of the game was too demanding for his tastes. Peters liked the trappings of success but only if they came his way through a deal.

As a manufacturers' rep, his sales territory included the Tech Heaven franchise where Jamie was a top salesman. He represented several large Asian consumer electronics manufacturers—some of them household names—as well as some more lucrative if obscure lesser names from emerging economies.

The two had met when Jamie won a sales contest sponsored by one of Al's manufacturers. Almost ten years Jamie's senior, the tall well-travelled urbane rep had taken Jamie under his wing during the trip, showing the younger man how expense accounts were meant to be managed.

Now on his second marriage, Al seldom hesitated to indulge in extracurricular dalliances on his travels, if not closer to home.

This would be his last call of the day. Jamie wasn't the senior salesman for the franchise, but Peters regarded him as his most likely ally and sought him out. Despite his relative youth, Peters enjoyed Jamie's self-deprecating humor and ready smile. If he'd ever had a daughter, he would have approved of any boyfriend with Jamie's dark curls, deep tan and lean athletic build.

"Jamie my boy," he slapped him on the back with some force. "Saw you on TV a few weeks back. Thought you could use some new lines to sell."

Jamie extracted himself from a conversation with a tire-kicker in the large-screen TV section. "Half my customers saw that show. Only now do they want to buy something from me."

"I'll bet," Al laughed. "Did you decide on your Findependence Day yet?"

"As a matter of fact, I did."

"Let me give you the secret of building wealth. Forget being a salaried employee. Get out there and start a business. Be an owner."

"I get the 'be an owner, not a loaner' thing," Jamie replied, "so I've been reading about equity mutual funds as a way to get a piece of the action."

"You think Bill Gates or Warren Buffett got rich investing in mutual funds?" scoffed Al. "They started companies. They concentrated their wealth in one business and made the big score."

"And we hear about them every day. But it takes a hundred losers to make a millionaire. We don't hear about the people who tried and failed. Or thousands of small business owners who make a nice, comfortable living."

Al noticed Jamie's boss, Jharhid, walk by. He smiled as Jamie pretended to straighten out the shelves of expensive MP3 player accessories Al was repping.

"Seems you're still working for the man yourself," Jamie said, gesturing towards the numerous shelves of techno-toys.

"True, but I've got serious stuff going on the side and big plans." Al glanced at his gold Rolex and added: "Isn't your shift over soon?"

Jamie checked his cellphone display, which he used instead of a watch. "20 minutes."

"I'm knocking off. Join me for a cocktail at the Moonshadow next door?"

Jamie looked uncomfortable.

"I'd rather not. I'm on a bit of an austerity kick."

"Know all about that. Don't sweat it. I have a few business opportunities I'd like to bounce off you. See you in 20 minutes then?"

Jamie nodded.

■ ■ ■

Al greeted the Korean hostess in her native tongue and ordered a double scotch. By the time Jamie arrived, he was on his second.

"What can I get you?" Al asked, signalling the waitress.

"A beer. Hite Prime."

"You call Sheena?"

"I said I might be a little late. Important business."

"You'd be right. You play poker?"

Jamie grinned and Al knew he'd found one of Jamie's hot buttons.

"Sure. Mostly online."

"That's not poker. That's kid stuff. See those guys over there?"

Al pointed out a table with three well-dressed Asian businessmen.

"They're all big players in our business. Know where the big deals happen?"

Jamie shrugged.

"In a smoky room late at night over the poker table. Here, I'll introduce you."

Al dragged Jamie over to the table. Bowing slightly towards the older man, Al smiled.

"Gentlemen, this is Jamie Morelli, an important associate at Tech Heaven *and* a television personality."

Names and business cards were exchanged. "My friend is also an avid poker player. Is the game on tonight?"

A friendly bespectacled man named Jimon nodded enthusiastically.

"Don't let us disturb you. We'll drop by later for a few hands," Al said.

Back at their table, the waitress dropped off more drinks. "Stick with me and you'll pay off those credit cards in no time. I've been running my own import business on the side the last few years, learning the ropes. I've got it nailed: great suppliers in some hot market and I've scored on some big no-name deals. You could get your bonus commission in shares. Everybody wins!" Al failed to mention that "no-name" really meant "knock-off" counterfeit goods, for which he was essentially the fence.

Jamie looked unconvinced and refilled his glass.

"Call Sheena to say you're having dinner," Al continued. "You can honestly say you're making important business connections."

Jamie stepped outside to place the call. Through the window, Al could see the glow of Jamie's cell phone against the dusk.

When he returned, Jamie gave the thumbs-up sign. Two hours later when the bill was presented Al thanked the hostess in Korean, but didn't reach for his wallet.

"I'm sure Jharhid will sign off on this," Al shoved the check across the table. "You have an entertainment account?"

"Not yet."

"Don't worry about it. Get in on the ground floor of my new business and you won't have to worry about such minor expenses. Give us some good shelf position and I'll take care of you."

Reluctantly, Jamie tossed a card into the tray. Al didn't recognize it.

"Good thing Sheena didn't let Didi cut them all up,' Al said.

"This is a new one," Jamie admitted. "Spend 'n Save."

The poker went on until 3 a.m. Jamie was down on the night while Al felt flush enough to give him a lift home.

Chapter 4

Baby You're a Rich Man

[THE BEATLES, 1967]

By the time Saturday morning rolled around, Jamie's headache had subsided to a tolerable level. Sheena was not amused when he told her the $195 bar bill had been rounded up to $200 and $5 deposited into the savings account.

In return for cutting back her own spending, she had extracted a promise from him that he'd cut back on various expenses, including visiting sports bars after work. They made a pact to become "frugality guerrillas," a term Sheena soon shortened to "Froogers."

Instead of sending his shirts to the cleaners, Jamie now ironed them while watching ball games. As another part of the Frooger campaign, Jamie planned to curtail his habit of buying new Compact Discs or downloading tunes into his MP3 players. As an aspiring songwriter, Jamie would never illegally download music but at a dollar a track the bills soon mounted up paying for iTunes and similar services.

The Vinyl Cave mentioned by Theo intrigued him.

He'd learned from the high-end audiophiles who came into Tech Heaven to buy turntables that the little record store had a solid reputation. Mostly aging baby boomers, these customers, known as "vinyl purists," claimed to find the sound quality on CDs excruciating. And the music sound quality on computer hard drives and portable audio devices was even worse. Vinyl had long been supplanted by CDs and MP3s, but the little store bucked the trend to digital music.

The Vinyl Cave occupied the ground floor and basement of an old two-storey commercial strip in a busy thoroughfare in the west end of town. The sign was easy to miss but the plate glass window was plastered with famous arty album covers from the 1960s and 1970s. Some of these Jamie recognized from the covers of reissued CD versions: the ethereal blue "On the Threshold of a Dream" cover from the Moody Blues and others of that ilk.

"Are you Bernie?" Jamie asked the person manning an ancient cash register. He was an aging hippie in faded blue jeans and a tie-died T-shirt. He was balding rapidly but still sported a short grey ponytail.

"I am." Jamie picked out an old Byrds LP and one from Crosby, Stills & Nash. "How much?"

"Everything in the bins is $2." Bernie coughed, vigorously enough that he covered his mouth with an old blue bandana. "Less if in really bad shape. Collectors' items over there are priced separately but are quite a bit more."

Bernie walked him to a nearby set of bins.

"Any Beatles or Stones?"

Bernie looked him over, amused. "Can't get them on vinyl any more in stores like this. If you're lucky enough to find them at a yard sale, I'd be delighted to buy them from you."

"How much?"

"Playable, $100. Mint condition, sky's the limit." Bernie stretched an arm upwards to underline the point.

"You must be kidding. I came here to save money."

"You can if you stay away from the big obvious acts. We've got plenty of Jethro Tull at regular prices, Eagles, Poco—those kinds of groups."

"I like Tull. I have their greatest hits on CD," Jamie said.

Bernie scrunched up his face. "Unlistenable, like most CDs. You can get Tull's first ten original vinyl releases, including cover art and liner notes, for $20 total," Bernie said.

"I'd be lucky to get just one of their CDs for that price."

"Genesis and Led Zeppelin are getting pricey if you can find them at all. You have a turntable?"

"No, but I can get a brand new Sony one at a discount through work. Do you have PFM or I Pooh? My older brother used to listen to those great Italian rock bands on vinyl back in the 70s."

"PFM?"

"Premiata Forneria Marconi. Maybe you remember their album, *Photos of Ghosts*?"

"Now I remember," Bernie said. "Used to have them but someone cleaned them out. Happens with some of these lesser known bands." He shrugged, making a "what can you do?" gesture with his hands.

"Too bad. I'll take the Tulls," Jamie said, brandishing a $20 bill. "Bet you can't even download most of these tunes. How's the sound quality?"

Bernie took one of the albums out of the jacket and held the shining black disc so the light bounced off it.

"There may be a few clicks and pops but at this price you can't go wrong. Far better than the skipping of a CD player. The sound of a needle on a groove is much more pure, deeper."

Bernie paused, apparently uncertain how much Jamie wanted to know. Jamie gave him an encouraging nod. Bernie took a drag of a cigarette that had been smouldering on an old black ashtray on the counter.

"Analog is how the human ear works," he continued, coughing again. "Digital sound is the biggest fraud ever perpetrated on the unwashed masses."

Motioning to another customer who had just entered the shop, he said, "But don't take my word for it. My friend will tell you the same."

"Bernie, put out that smoke." A casually dressed man in a plaid shirt and khakis waved his hand to clear the blue haze. It was Theo, the financial advisor who'd appeared with Jamie on Didi's show.

"Mr. Konstantin," Jamie extended his hand. "We meet again."

"Theo," the older man responded. "Call me Theo. Didn't expect to find you here."

"Price is right," Jamie gestured at the garish hand-written $2 and $5 "as is" signs. "I promised Sheena I'd cut back on CDs and downloading music."

"How much have you been spending on it?"

"Three or four hundred a month, including my weekend outings at Louie's Sports Bar. It's all classified as Entertainment."

Theo gave him an approving look. "Glad to hear you're tracking expenses and making a budget. Big step." He stepped towards one of the display cases and started thumbing through some albums.

"I haven't bought a CD in two weeks," Jamie said, "and I'm brown bagging it to work. The music here is amazing."

Theo smiled. "The golden age of rock and roll."

"I missed it all. I grew up when CDs first came out. The big bands were Duran Duran and Culture Club."

"I feel your pain," Theo said, picking through the records. He selected one. "Now here's a classic."

He handed Jamie an album by Renaissance. "Annie Haslam. Angelic voice. Just did a song with the reunited Asia."

"Don't know 'em. Exhausted my budget," Jamie said, pointing to his bag of Jethro Tull LPs.

"Didi really got under your skin, didn't she?" After a pause, Theo added: "Tell me, do you and Sheena have the same views on spending and investments?"

"We both like spending but I'd like to start investing. She'd rather shop."

"Ever talk about retirement?" Theo was reading the liner notes on the back of the Renaissance album.

"Who does in their 20s? Sheena has a great pension plan and could retire at 55. She just has to hang in until her age and service equals 85."

"So she's set. How about you? Does your employer have a Defined Contribution pension or group plan?"

Jamie imitated Theo, flipping through a second row of albums, few of which he recognized. "Don't know. The second, I think. A group plan. If you sign up for the maximum deduction Tech Heaven will do some kind of 5% matching. It's optional so I passed."

"If it's a DC pension, they can't guarantee a set retirement income after you stop working. They promise only to put in a set amount of money into the plan each month, hence the phrase Defined Contribution. How much they pay out at the end will depend on how the stock market does."

"That's the one. There were too many decisions to make so I never filled out the paperwork."

"That was unwise. When your employer offers you a pension plan—especially with matching contributions—it's free money. You'd be crazy not to take it."

Theo pulled out another album. "I always liked this cover." It showed a grand piano set before a majestic mountain landscape.

"Supertramp's *Even in the Quietest Moments*," Jamie recognized it from his CD version. "Victor played that to death when it came out in 1977."

"Victor?"

"My older brother. He still lives in the States. We both loved that song *From Now On*."

"When I was a working stiff decades away from freedom, I related to that one as well," Theo nodded, and sang a snippet of the opening lyric, "Monnnnnday has come around again…."

"My theme song," Jamie grinned. "That's why I need you to chart my road to Financial Independence. Your rich clients don't need you as much as I do."

"You may be richer than you think. The banks have it right on that score."

"That's just a marketing line."

"It is. But what they're really referring to is Human Capital. You're a young man with decades of earning potential ahead of you. I'd guess a couple of million dollars worth."

"Never thought of it that way."

"I on the other hand have only a few more years of earning ahead of me but have spent the last three decades converting my human capital into financial capital."

"Are you a Greek tycoon?"

"A gentleman never tells," Theo said lightly. "Neither does a tycoon. Tell me. Are you a stock or a bond?"

Jamie put the album back on the shelf.

"What do you mean?"

"That's the title of a book[1] by a noted university finance professor, Dr. Moshe Milevsky. Just as some people love classical music and some love pop, some investors are like stocks, while others are bonds."

"Not sure I get it."

"Take Sheena," Theo said. "She has a steady job and a good pension with a strong union. If she teaches for 30 years, she's guaranteed a steady regular pension income for life so I'd call her a bond. Which means, ironically, that when she gets serious about investing in a few years, she could take more risk by investing in equity."

"And me?"

"You're on commission?" Theo started to walk to the back of the store.

"Mostly, but there's a base salary." Jamie followed him to the classical section. The further they got from the storefront window, the dimmer it got. Some old fluorescent bulbs were flickering on and off.

---

[1] See appendix, A Peek at Theo's Library

"Plan to stay long at Tech Heaven?"

"Who knows? Sheena is talking about having kids so I may be longer there than I think. One day, though, I'd like to go out on my own."

"You sound like a stock since there's more risk in your job and more opportunity for reward. But you should still enrol in the company pension and take their 5% matching offer."

Theo stopped in front of some classical music box sets.

"The pension offers 17 different mutual funds," Jamie said, "How do I know which to pick?"

"Since your job and lifestyle are riskier, like a stock, you should have relatively more fixed income. But if you invest systematically, you could invest your biweekly pension contributions mostly in equities: over many years systematic contributions reduces portfolio volatility, just like fixed income."

Theo picked up a Baroque box set with a red cover. "What a steal: Time-Life's *The Story of Great Music*. Worth the ten bucks for the books alone." He opened it up and showed him four mint pieces of vinyl and two booklets.

Jamie glanced at the box set.

"I'm not a classical music guy and I'm not into bonds. I like melodic rock and stocks. Be an owner, not a loaner. I want to start a stock portfolio as soon as I can. That's what I'll do with the money I save by shopping here."

Theo looked skeptical.

"I wouldn't obsess about retirement saving just now. Sign up for the company pension, certainly, but at your age you should put all your disposable income into debt reduction. From what I've seen, that alone should take up the rest of your 20s."

"Victor started his Individual Retirement Account in his late 20s. He doesn't find saving in an IRA to be a huge burden because of the tax savings he gets. I'd like to start my own tax-sheltered retirement plan as soon as I can."

"Commendable strategy. In this country, that would be a Registered Retirement Savings Plan. We call them RRSPs." Theo put a third set of classical box sets under his arm and began walking to the front of the store.

"But I need someone to help me pick what goes into it. You'd be the perfect guy."

"Call me when the plastic is off your back and the mortgage is paid down."

"Mortgage? We're still renting. We can't do everything at once."

"Precisely my point. So forget about tax-sheltered retirement plans and stock portfolios for now and focus on getting out of debt. Many people don't get serious about investing until their mid-30s. You still have lots of time."

Bernie, who had been listening to the tail end of the conversation, nodded.

"You agree, Bernie?" Theo placed his purchases on the cluttered counter.

"Absolutely." Bernie nodded. "Spend less than you earn and get the plastic monkey off your back."

Theo turned to Jamie. "I told you Bernie is a part-time fee-only financial planner. You taking new clients?"

Bernie nodded again, handing Jamie a business card that was printed on both sides. One side showed him as the owner of the Vinyl Cave, the other as a certified financial planner.

Frugal. This is our guy.

"We'll talk," said Jamie.

■ ■ ■

Winter had fallen and Jamie was relaxing in the den, listening to his latest purchases from the Vinyl Cave. They sounded phenomenal on the new turntable he'd wired into his surround sound system.

The pension update Tech Heaven had given him after he'd finally completed the paperwork was a depressing read. He would be eligible to begin drawing pension benefits in 30 more years. Jamie tossed it on the table in disgust. *I'm not sure I can stand three more years of this, let alone 30.*

"There's got to be a faster way," he muttered under his breath.

"Did you say something, honey?" Sheena had just poked her head into the den. "Supper in ten minutes."

"I was just looking at my new pension statements," he said, pointing to the envelope. "What are the odds I'll stay long enough to collect it?"

Picking her way carefully through stacked cartons of LPs and 45s, Sheena crossed the cluttered room. Opening the envelope, she pored over the contents for a minute. "Knowing you, not great but it appears to be portable."

"Portable?"

"Even if you leave, you can take it with you. Transfer it into your personal retirement account and add to it."

"How did you become such an expert on pensions all of a sudden?"

"Teachers' union. I read the brochures. Anyway, you're really not as locked in to the endless grind as I am."

"That's a relief. I doubt I'll be at Tech Heaven much longer."

"Got an offer you can't refuse?"

"I've been thinking about what Theo told me about business ownership and equities."

"Theo? Thought we weren't rich enough to become his clients?"

"We're not but I sometimes bump into him at the Vinyl Cave." Jamie gestured to a couple of albums strewn on the coffee table. Sheena gave him a disapproving look.

"He always seems happy to give me a tip or two about investing and financial planning."

"What is the great financial wizard's latest insight?"

"Remember how I told you about you being a bond and me being a stock?"

"Sure." Sheena stooped to tidy the coffee table, grabbing a newspaper and an empty glass.

"He asked me how I felt about holding a mutual fund that owns a small piece of hundreds of businesses, versus starting up my own."

"And?" she yelled from the kitchen, putting the glass into the dishwasher.

"I said I could see doing both. Early in life you build a business, like Bill Gates or Michael Dell. Or mum and dad with the restaurant."

She stood in the door between the kitchen and the den, hands on her hips. "Big versus small business. Major difference."

"All big enterprises started small." Jamie got up from the couch to flip the album over. *Now that's one thing I don't miss with CDs.* "When you build it up and sell out, you diversify into a bunch of other people's businesses. That's the beauty of equity mutual funds or, these days, ETFs."

"ETFs. Is that some new kind of electronic funds transfer?"

"Not EFT, ETF. It stands for exchange-traded funds. The way Theo explained it, an ETF is similar to a mutual fund but trades on a stock exchange like any individual stock. But it costs a lot less for the investor."

"And I care because…?" She turned off the burners beneath two pots.

"You care because you're married to a risk-taking entrepreneurial kind of guy. One who plans to stop being an employee for some other entrepreneur and start up a business of his own some day. Maybe it will be listed on the New York Stock Exchange and those mutual funds and ETFs will own tiny bits of that business."

"How does this help us Froogers save money?"

"Right now it won't. But ETFs charge lower fees than mutual funds because they don't pay high-priced investment managers to research and buy individual stocks. They just buy whatever index you want to track."

"Index?" Sheena didn't seem to be paying much attention.

"Like the Standard & Poor's 500 index. An index fund or ETF tracking the S&P500 index would give you a tiny ownership position in 500 publicly traded companies in leading industries in the United States trading on that index."

Sheena shrugged and changed the subject. "What are you listening to now?"

"Strawbs. *Grave New World.*"

"Must be vinyl: I hear a scratch."

"You don't notice after a while. It's a mellower sound than CDs, don't you think?"

"Guess so. How much of this junk have you bought the last six months? Must be adding up."

"Not a lot. Most cost just $2 each. Think of it as an investment. This hobby could pay for itself. Remember what I said about business ownership? Take a look at this."

Jamie picked up one of the albums from the coffee table. The jacket opened up to an artistic two-page spread, plus there was a lyric sheet and a poster.

"You're telling me all this—plus the music—is worth only a couple of bucks? The baby boomers are retiring. When they do, they're going to fill their cottages with nostalgic stuff from their youth. Prices of these old records will skyrocket. Even without the music itself some of the art covers may fetch a pretty penny."

Sheena looked dubious as she put a salad on the dining room table. "Can you set the table please?"

Jamie pretended not to hear. "I can flip this for more than three times what I paid for it."

"I don't see any buyers pounding on our door."

"Mail order. Sell them on eBay. And that's not all. Take a look at this." Jamie angled his laptop so Sheena could see the display.

"My new web site, Vinyl Nation."

"Since when were you a web designer?"

"I'm not, but Jharhid's son is. He's still a student and hardly charged me anything to get the site up. Look, here's the chat room."

Sheena peeked at the screen. It said 14 users were online. There appeared to be a heated discussion between a cyber identity called Nimrod and another called Shankshaft about how the Doors' Jim Morrison died.

"Banner ads," Jamie whispered, "It's only a matter of time before sponsors line up to reach this audience."

"Who? The makers of Geritol and Sominex?"

Jamie ignored the jibe. The kid had done a great job on the web design. The site's Fifties look matched the content: LPs, 45s and cover art.

"Here's where they can order albums."

Sheena looked. "Ten dollars each?"

"Plus shipping and handling of $4. Remember, my cost from Bernie is just two bucks for most albums. I save my customers hours of searching through bins in dimly lit basements. On Vinyl Nation, they just click and buy."

"You're kidding yourself if you think a bunch of boomer geezers will pay ten bucks for junk they can find at any garage sale." Sheena stepped forward, her foot grazing a box of old records parked on the floor. "Even if they wanted to buy them, look at this place. I can't even walk through any more."

"I was meaning to talk to you about that. Now I've told you how I can turn this hobby into a small business, why don't we make the spare bedroom our base of operations?"

"No way. The spare room is spoken for." She went back to the kitchen, loaded the plates and put them on the dining room table.

Jamie finally got the hint and set the table.

"What do you mean spoken for?"

"Where do you think junior is going to sleep?"

"Are you saying …" In shock, Jamie looked up at his slim young wife.

"I'm not pregnant but I intend to be before I'm 30." The note of finality in her usually soft voice was matched by a glint of flint in her eyes. "Bon appetit."

Jamie poured some red wine and they clinked glasses.

"When that happens, the extra bedroom is going to be properly decorated for Morelli Minor."

"But until then…?"

"Until then, you can get this junk out of here. Keep one box of the stuff you actually listen to. But no way are you're running a mail-order business from this cramped little apartment."

"To an entrepreneur a problem is just an opportunity in disguise," Jamie replied.

■ ■ ■

Near the end of the year, Jamie and Sheena were invited to Al's annual pre-Christmas party. This was the first time they had been included, and Jamie was under no illusion as to why he was on the list. Part TV celeb, part Tech Heaven contact, part go-fer, Jamie knew he could be useful to Al.

As he turned his old Firebird into the long driveway, Sheena let out an involuntary gasp.

"It's enormous," she said. A gentle snow was falling but the lights illuminating the half-mile road added to the overall impression of opulence. A giant evergreen on the lawn was lit up with hundreds of bulbs, all of them blue. Through the door of a large redbrick garage at the end, Jamie could just make out Al's Lexus and a Porsche.

The house had to be 7,000 square feet, nestled in front of a sprawling woodlot. Snow outlined the beautifully sculpted lines of junipers, cedars and dried hydrangeas of a professionally landscaped garden.

"I didn't know manufacturers' reps made this kind of money," Jamie whispered, as he rang the doorbell.

"Ten to one it's all borrowed."

"He's got business deals going on the side."

"I bet he does."

"You've always resented my relationship with Al. You're just upset about all the time I spend with him."

"And the poker... and the drinking," Sheena snapped. "I wouldn't call Al a frugality guerrilla."

Jamie grinned: "He's the furthest thing from a Frooger!"

A small elderly woman opened the big oak door. They stepped into a brightly lit three-story foyer that could have swallowed up their whole apartment. Another Christmas tree—this one artificial—sparkled with multi-colored bulbs and tinsel. Jamie figured the foyer's heating bill alone would eclipse a year's worth of utility bills at the condo.

They joined a crowd of partiers around the bar in the adjoining great room. Al was regaling a group of business people, some of whom Jamie recognized from the poker nights. While the invitation had said business casual, Al was wearing a tuxedo, complete with red cummerbund and flashy gold cufflinks. He was just delivering the punch line to one of his favourite—and oft-told—jokes. It had the desired effect. One guest nearly choked on his beer. Another sputtered and turned red in the face.

"Jamie," Al now noticed him. "Thank you for coming to our little shindig. I believe you already know some of these folks? You remember Riki and Jimon from our poker nights?"

"I do." Jamie acknowledged two of Al's associates with a nod. "This is my wife, Sheena."

"She is also television celebrity?" Jimon asked. His thick black glasses masked his thoughts as effectively as the smile that flitted across his face, even when he was losing money at poker.

"I wouldn't go that far, though Sheena is writing a book for teens," Jamie replied. Delighted at the chance to talk to an attractive media star and author, the two began chatting with Sheena.

As the evening progressed, the light classical music in the foyer gave way to a live jazz trio with a smooth swing sound. The alcohol was flowing liberally. The rising crescendo of laughter and music made conversation increasingly difficult.

Strolling into another large room of the house, Jamie caught Al's eye. "I could use another drink."

"Let me help you," Al said, taking Jamie's arm and guiding him to a secondary bar staffed by two black-tied young men.

"My nephew and stepson," Al whispered. After they were served, Al took Jamie into a nearby office. "I sense you wanted some privacy," he explained. "You have a proposition?"

"You're a mind reader. I need a favour."

"Shoot."

"I have a minor storage problem for a mail-order business I'm trying to get off the ground. There's no room in the condo and—"

Jamie looked Al squarely in the face but it was inscrutable. Uncertain whether to proceed, he stammered, "I need to lease space in a real commercial building: not a lot of space."

Jamie's face flushed.

Al said: "Not sure I follow. What do you want me to do?"

"I'm a little short on capital," Jamie said, still flustered. "I need to come up with first and last month's rent on some space I've identified."

"I see." Distractedly, Al looked through the door at some guests who had strayed near the room.

"Even a home-based mail-order business looks more impressive with a real business address, doesn't it?" Jamie stammered.

"Of course," Al said absent-mindedly. "Business 101."

"Bottom line is it would be helpful if I could borrow ten grand from you just to get this going." As soon as the words came out of his mouth, Jamie regretted it.

Al took a swig of his beer and considered this. Then he shook his head. "Don't think so, Jamie. I'd like to help you but—"

"No sweat. It was just an idea," Jamie interrupted him and turned to leave.

"...Hear me out. The reason I can't lend you the money is I have some cash-flow issues of my own."

Jamie gave him a quizzical expression. "Look at this place," he said. "When Sheena and I drove up your huge driveway, we were amazed. If you can afford all this—"

"I'm building wealth certainly, but not much of it is liquid," Al replied. "What cash I do have is earmarked for a business venture of my own."

Al looked up at the ceiling. "In fact," he said after a long pause, "there may even be a role for you to play." He reached for Jamie's arm.

"Go on."

"My connections have identified some electronics manufacturers in China that could undercut the brand-name majors that sell into Tech Heaven and its rivals."

"That's nice, but our customers value the big established brands, their support and warranties. They're happy to pay a premium price."

Al considered this before continuing. "I'm talking a possible piece of the action."

"Equity?"

"What else? This is just getting off the ground. It would be your chance to get in early."

"I'd have to talk to Sheena first."

"Do that. Better get back to her now. You know how Riki and Jimon can be with attractive women after a few drinks."

Al steered his young friend back through the throng of guests to the foyer. Sheena was standing in a corner by herself. She didn't look happy.

"What's with the long face?" He'd seen those beautiful compressed lips before. Invariably they indicated her displeasure with something he'd said or done.

"I don't like your poker friends."

"They're nice guys when you get to know them."

"They were trying to get to know me alright. The moment you took off with Al, Riki had his hand on my backside. He creeped me out."

Jamie's face darkened. "He may have had too much to drink."

"Please, let's leave."

Jamie began to protest but well knew that look. He was not inclined to test Sheena's Irish temperament and made an unconvincing excuse to their startled host. They retrieved their coats and boots from a hall closet that was the size of their master bedroom and exited quickly.

The car was covered with a light film of snow and the roads were slippery. Jamie drove well below the speed limit. As he did, he recounted the gist of his chat with Al.

"What kind of business deal?"

"Importing electronics. He's well connected and has found a few ultra-low-cost suppliers in China."

"What does he need you for?"

"An entrée into Tech Heaven, I guess."

"You're not high enough up to help him are you?"

"No, but there are a few things I could do to grease the wheels."

"Sounds like a conflict. I'd steer clear of any business deals with Al Peters and his sleaze ball friends."

Jamie gripped the steering wheel more tightly as the silence between them grew.

"Besides, none of this solves your storage problem," Sheena said after more minutes had passed.

Jamie nodded, taking his eye off the road long enough to glance at Sheena.

"There's more than one way to skin that cat."

Chapter 5

You Can't Always Get What You Want

[THE ROLLING STONES, 1969]

The New Year was a few weeks old and Jamie hadn't bumped into Theo at the Vinyl Cave or anywhere else. Concerned about seeming too pushy, Jamie was pleased when his new acquaintance and his wife Ariana accepted an invitation to join them for dinner at the condo. Partly converted to the Froogers' austerity program, Sheena had added a number of low-cost but tasty meals to her repertoire.

Jamie greeted Theo and Ariana at the door. As Jamie hung Ariana's fur coat in the closet, he was struck by how she was able to combine elegance with simplicity. Theo and Ariana seemed well matched.

Her apron still on, Sheena walked into the narrow hallway to greet them.

"Theo, Ariana," Jamie said, "I'm so glad you could join us. You remember Sheena?"

"Certainly," Theo said, delivering a light peck on Sheena's cheek. "And this is my wife Ariana," he smiled.

The obligatory tour of the condo took all of three minutes. Sheena allowed their guests only a quick peek through the door of the disordered spare room. Jamie apologized. "I'm trying to get a mail-order business off the ground."

"From small acorns grow great oak trees," Theo smiled approvingly, as they took their places in the dining room. "You're in the market for your first home?"

Jamie opened up a bottle of Italian red, presenting it to Theo for his approval. He seemed amused but obliged by pouring a bit in his glass, raising it to his nose and sniffing, all in a deliberately exaggerated fashion. "Perfetto."

"We hope to buy this condo from our landlords," Sheena said, placing a hot pot of Irish stew in the centre of the table. "They bought during the boom, hoping to flip it. The way the market is I'm sure they'll give us a good price."

"They may," Theo said. "I regard a paid-up home as the cornerstone of Financial Independence. How is your program to reduce debt coming along?"

"Not as fast as we'd like," Jamie said. "But the department store cards are all paid off."

"As they should be. They get you with an in-store promotion and no interest for six months then sock it to you with exorbitant interest rates."

Jamie and Sheena exchanged sheepish glances, remembering the bedroom furniture.

"As for the rest, have you considered taking a line of credit and consolidating all your outstanding loans?" Theo continued.

"We did that already." Sheena said, ladling out more stew.

"I was never a math whiz at school, but even I know it would be better to pay interest under 10% on one loan than 18% or 25% on a bunch of credit cards," said Jamie.

"Glad to hear it," Theo said, "Especially when those interest charges aren't tax deductible. You want to get rid of all forms of bad debt."

"All debt is bad, isn't it?" Jamie said.

"Not necessarily, but non-tax-deductible consumer debt at high interest charges certainly falls into the category of bad debt."

"Is there such a thing as good debt?" Sheena asked.

"I'm conservative, so I think the best debt is no debt at all," Theo said. "Most retirees should be debt-free by the time they end their working years. But for young people like yourselves, I'd consider a mortgage on your first home to be good debt."

"Especially if it's also tax deductible," Jamie said. "Victor can write off all his mortgage interest against his taxes."

"That's one advantage Americans have over Canadians. You can't do that in Canada even on your main residence. But that may be a mixed blessing. Because of the tax deductibility, many Americans take decades to pay off their mortgages."

"What a great write-off!" Sheena said.

"Perhaps, but what they save in taxes they lose in extra interest charges. Or they get too much house and end up overextended. Many who lost their homes to foreclosure found that out after the subprime mortgage crisis."

"But that was the States," Ariana said, looking at her husband in amusement.

"Don't kid yourself. It could happen here, though on a smaller scale. The best strategy is simply to pay off the mortgage as fast as possible. Once you do, you can start investing seriously in a diversified equity portfolio."

Jamie refilled the glasses with generous amounts of wine, but Ariana put her hand on top of her glass. "Just water. I'm driving tonight," she explained.

Jamie gave her an understanding look and glanced back at Theo.

"What about the Smith Manoeuvre?"

"What's that?" Sheena asked.

"Ah, the Smith Manoeuvre," Theo laughed, taking a big sip of wine. "For those who want to have their cake and eat it too by making their mortgage tax-deductible, just like the Americans."

He explained how a movement had sprung up on the west coast in which financial planners structured mortgage payments in a way that gradually paid off the mortgage while adding to a stock portfolio.

"I prefer what I call the Half Smith," Theo said, "which is the oldest idea in the mortgage world. Simply pay down your mortgage as fast as possible."

"How?" Sheena asked.

"How much would you expect to pay for this condo?" Theo asked. He gestured with a sweep of his arm.

"Say $300,000," Jamie offered.

"Okay. At today's interest rates, when you first start a regular 25-year mortgage, what would you expect to pay per month?"

"$2,000?" Sheena asked.

"Close enough. At 6.65% it would be $2,037 but let's work with $2,000 to keep it simple. How much of that would be interest payments?"

"$1,640?"

"And just $397 of principal. So after a year, how much interest have you paid?"

Jamie whipped out a pocket calculator and tapped out: "12 times $1,640, or $19,680."

"And how much principal have you paid off the original $300,000?"

"That's easy, said Sheena, "12 times $400 or $4,800."

"So after a year, how much do you still owe?"

"$300,000 minus $4,800, or $295,200," Sheena said, her face clouding, "That doesn't seem fair."

"Right. So after a year you've paid out more than $24,000 but only reduced your mortgage by $4,800. That's the reality of mortgage amortizations," Theo said.

"That doesn't sound any better than renting," Jamie said. "Maybe we should just stay put here."

Theo accepted Sheena's offer of more bread and sipped some wine before proceeding.

"If you stay here you'll be renting forever, and landlords will keep raising your rent. They have to keep up with inflation too."

"But it will take forever to pay down a mortgage too," Jamie said. He got up to change the music. "How about some Handel?" He retrieved the Baroque box set he'd purchased on his last excursion to the Vinyl Cave.

Theo raised his thumb to signal his approval. "Fine wine and fine music. Now if we can just get your finances fine."

"Isn't the literal meaning of mortgage in the original French payment until death?" Jamie asked.

"That's right," Theo said, impressed with the youngster's linguistic knowledge. "Mort is death and gage is pledge. And it might take that long if you do what the banks want and extend your amortization to 30 or even 35 years. What you want is to go in the other direction, amortize the mortgage loan over just 10 or 15 years."

"How do we do that?" Jamie adjusted the volume on his stereo as the first notes of the Water Music floated through the room.

"There are various tools that will help you figure out how much you can save on interest by accelerating your mortgage. But you can do it yourself just by taking advantage of the prepayment privilege."

"Which is?

"On any payment date, you can make an extra payment of 10% to 25% of the original principal. That payment goes directly to paying down principal so it has a dramatic effect on reducing interest charges over the long run. In our example, 15% of $300,000 is $45,000. If you paid that, what would your principal remaining be after a year?"

"The earlier $295,200 minus $45,000, which is a little over $250,000," Sheena said.

"And if you did that for four more years?"

"About $80,000, maybe less."

"Right: $79,192 to be precise, according to Amortization.com. What if you hadn't done the annual prepayment? What would the $300,000 be down to after five years?"

"It would still be more than $275,000."

"Huge difference, right? The beauty is that, in the second example, more and more payments will be going to further principal reduction, instead of interest. Early in a mortgage amortization, your payments are more than 80% interest. Later in the cycle, they may be 80% principal. That's why it's so important to pay it down quickly, especially in the early years. The more you pay off early, the less you pay altogether."

"But where do we get the $45,000 a year?" Jamie said.

"There's the rub. You're both working, aren't you?"

"Yes, but life is expensive." Jamie winked at Sheena. He covered his mouth so only she could see what he was saying as he whispered: "Guerrilla frugality."

"This is why I keep suggesting you watch your expenses," Theo said. He seemed aware of Jamie's aside but chose to ignore it, "If you want Findependence, you have to make a habit of being frugal. As Didi says, guerrilla frugality is not something you do one day and cast off the next." Jamie's eyes met Sheena's as she giggled.

"It's the little things that start to add up," Jamie said. "For instance, I've stopped buying lottery tickets when I pick up milk from the corner store."

"And he's stopped player poker for money," Sheena said. "Now he just plays online for fun."

"Good. Frugality is a lifelong attitude to money," Theo said. He couldn't resist pronouncing 'frugality' with a parody of a Scot's accent. "You have to spend less than you earn, year in and year out."

"How much less?"

"With both of you working, aim for 20%. Your mantra upon waking every morning must be 'spend less than you earn.' If you don't you'll be a slave to the banks and your employers forever."

"Pay yourself first," Jamie said. "Wasn't that what *The Richest Man in Babylon* was all about?"

"Yes. George Clason published that in 1926. Modern books[2] like *The Wealthy Barber* or *The Automatic Millionaire* preach the same thing—establish a savings and

[2]See appendix, A Peek at Theo's Library

investment program. Ideally, you set up a Pre-Authorized Chequing account or PAC and automatically transfer 10 or 20% of your paycheque into your investments."

"The idea being that money you never see won't be missed?"

"Exactly. It's automatic and less painful. Best of all it eliminates the temptation of putting consumption ahead of it. Logically such a program should follow the elimination of debt and the acquisition of a home. By spending 20% less than you earn, you can take those savings and slap it against your mortgage once a year."

"But you said you can do both with the Smith Manoeuvre?" Jamie said as he helped Sheena clear the main course plates.

"In theory yes, but as I said I prefer a Half Smith. Just pay down the mortgage, take advantage of the annual prepayment I just mentioned and make high weekly payments."

"*High* weekly payments?" Sheena said, serving salad after the main course.

"Yes, there's a slight advantage to paying weekly. And you *want* the bank to make your payments higher. All the extra payment goes straight down on principal, as in the annual prepayment option."

"Why is that a Half Smith?"

"I'm joking. Just pay it down substantially. Once you get to the point where at least half your payments are going to principal, then you can start thinking about the second half, which is investing."

"What about borrowing to invest?" Jamie asked.

"That's what the other half of the Smith Manoeuvre is about. It's based on another old idea. If you already had a big investment portfolio, say also $300,000, you could sell those stocks, use the proceeds to pay off the mortgage, then go to the bank and borrow another $300,000 to repurchase practically the same stocks.

"What's the point of that?"

Theo fixed Jamie with a professorial stare.

"The point is that when you borrow to invest you can deduct the interest from your taxable income. So it's a perfectly legal way to write off the interest on your stock purchases. You're borrowing to invest, and the Smith Manoeuvre is a complicated variant of that scheme. The problem is you and Sheena don't have a $300,000 stock portfolio and I don't think you're proper candidates for leverage."

"Leverage?" Sheena asked. She glanced at Ariana, who gave her a "what do I know?" look.

"Another term for borrowing to invest. In theory, leverage works. In practice, you need a lot of emotional fortitude to keep to the program when stock prices tumble, as they inevitably will from time to time. So my recommendation is buy an affordable first home and pay off the mortgage as fast as you can."

"I can see how that would speed up Findependence Day," Jamie said. "It's simple, but not very exciting."

"Leave exciting till later," Theo responded. "Do the simple, boring but hard stuff now and you're right, you can move your Findependence Day up by years."

Sheena made a face and turned back to Ariana to ask how her children were coping with university life. Theo got the hint and changed the subject. "How's the vinyl collection coming?"

"Come see," Jamie said. "I took you up on your suggestion and got all the Time-Life classical sets. I was surprised to discover lots of boomers on Vinyl Nation are classical buffs too."

Theo followed him into the den, stepping over some unfiled boxes of old records. Jamie powered up his computer and showed Theo the Vinyl Nation web site. On the chat site, the regulars—Old Hand, Nimrod, Princess and Shankshaft—were at it again discussing modern culture. "There seem to be two main clusters of interest," Jamie said. "Pop culture and Money. As you can see, there's great potential." Jamie gestured at the crowded room. "But I do have this storage problem."

"Not if you buy a bigger house."

"Sheena has her heart set on this condo, or at least a unit like it nearby."

An awkward pause, then Jamie decided to chance it. "Of course, if I had a business partner like you we could rent a small storage unit. That would also solve the problem."

Theo turned to his young friend with a short laugh.

"Forget it, Jamie. At my age, I don't need business partnerships."

Using his fingers to count them off, Jamie listed several reasons why Vinyl Nation had the potential to become a real business. Theo just shook his head.

"For me, adding to my vinyl collection is an enjoyable hobby. I find the analog sound more soothing to my ear than these new digital media," Theo said. "That's the sound I was raised on. CDs seem so harsh. So does digital music downloaded into portable units. But you have to face reality. The market has gone digital and any venture that revolves around these old relics can be nothing more than a hobby business."

Jamie took care not to let his face show how let down he felt.

"Besides," Theo continued, "I already have my own hobby business: my fee-only financial planning service. I can practise it remotely from my cottage up north."

"That's cool," Jamie said. "Can't blame a guy for trying."

"But it looks like an interesting community is developing in your chat room," Theo said, trying to sweeten the pill. "I'd be happy to drop in and add to the discussion from time to time."

■ ■ ■

It had been a stretch to come up with the initial $30,000 membership fee, but Al Peters believed the prestigious Lakeview Golf & Country Club was the price of entry to an elite world he soon intended to inhabit. Besides, what was the point of a big line of credit if you couldn't enjoy the finer things in life?

During one of his periodic sales visits to Tech Heaven in the spring, he casually dropped the fact of this membership into his conversation. Jamie looked impressed enough that Al extended an invitation to play a round of golf the following week-end. "We'll finish the day with a first-class meal at the clubhouse," he clinched the arrangement.

When it arrived, the day was bright. Al adjusted his Ray-Bans before setting his stance for his opening drive on the first tee.

"I hope the lovely Sheena enjoyed my little get-together last Christmas," he said, moments after lofting a fine 225-yarder on the par five.

"Very impressive place," Jamie said, badly topping his drive. "Mulligan?"

"Sure." Al sized his friend up. Jamie was wearing a light blue golf-shirt with a red eagle insignia, tan shorts and the mandatory white studded golf shoes. He looked good, with a deep tan matching his brown eyes and hair. But Al could always find fault with something. He decided Jamie's shorts looked dorky: he himself would stick with long pants no matter how hot it got.

"How long you two been married?"

"Four blissful years."

"If Sheena's still giving you a hard time over space, you can store your records in my basement. Just until you get your own place, understand?"

Jamie looked grateful. "That would help," he smiled.

"Anything to keep the little lady happy. Now if you'd like some extra happy in your life, there's a little hottie from the club I think you'd hit it off with. She just got her divorce finalized and I can tell you from personal experience she made me happy."

"Sheena is all the happy I want," Jamie said with a withering look.

They walked down the fairway, pulling their golf bags behind them in two-wheeled carriers. Al's approach shot cleared a water hazard and bounced on the green, a two-putt on a bad day.

"How's life in Tech Heaven?"

"Steady paycheque."

"Hanging in there for the micro-pension and gold watch?"

"Doubt it, Al, but with both of us earning steady income, it's a chance to estab-lish a firm financial foundation for the future. Besides, I get a buzz from sales when it's going well."

Al paused to line up his putt. "I sink this and it's a birdie."

He did and wrote down the score. "One over," Jamie said, "Not counting the Mulligan."

Al paused as they walked uphill to the next tee. He wiped the sweat off his fore-head with the back of his hand. "Maybe we should have taken a cart?"

"We need the exercise. Besides this is cheaper." Jamie looked trim and fit, Al had to admit.

Al picked out a driver and parked his clubs against a bench.

"How's that website and mail order business going?"

"Enough to write off some expenses."

"Ain't self employment wonderful? The last great tax shelter."

"Within reason, I guess. My accountant is careful not to go too far over the line mixing personal and business expenses."

"Right, and your accountant is a gazillionaire, right? Not!!"

Al hit another powerful drive, this one skidding off to the right of the fairway onto the edge of the rough.

"He does pretty well." Jamie squared up for his tee shot but Al thought his stance wasn't right.

"Like this," he said, showing how his feet were at exact right angles to the fairway. Jamie imitated him and got off a half-decent 150-yarder. "I don't play often enough," he excused himself.

"There are two kinds of people in this world," Al continued, "Bean counters and the people who make the beans. Which do you want to be?"

"I'm happy grinding out my day job and doing the odd thing on the side."

They were half way through a par four. Jamie cleared the green with a 3 iron on his third shot. "Should have gone with the 5 iron," he grimaced.

Al was on the green with his second shot. He putted and waited for Jamie to chip on to the green.

"So you could do a little freelance work on the side?"

"Sure. I don't think Jharhid would mind. Any extra income would go straight into paying down credit card debt."

"Very prudent."

"That's one of Theo's lessons."

There was a small refreshment stand on the way to the next hole. Al suggested they grab a couple of beverages.

"Theo?"

"My unofficial financial advisor."

Al nodded approvingly. "Moving up in the world," he said, handing the booth attendant a ten-dollar bill for his Corona and Jamie's Diet Coke.

"Just a friend who gives me a few tips. But he says leisure time doesn't have to be used spending money on more consumption. It can be used to earn additional income. Financial independence is a lifestyle choice."

"Glad to hear it,' Al said, handing Jamie his soda. "How are you at writing?"

"I've been doing a little blogging on my site, talking about music and pop culture."

"Does it pay?"

Jamie chuckled as he popped open the can. "Not hardly, but it's fun. I used to write song lyrics in high school when—"

Al gave him an ironic smile. "I know, during your rock star phase."

Jamie shrugged, a little embarrassed.

"Here's the thing," Al continued, taking a seat on a nearby bench. "I'm importing some new electronic gadgets and accessories from the Far East, but none of the material is in English. Think you could write some marketing copy for me? Brochures and handouts, that kind of thing?"

Jamie sat down beside him and took a swig of his soda.

"I could give it a whirl. Can you pay me?"

Al swept his hand expansively in the direction of the clubhouse. "If I can afford all this, I can pay you to write up some brochures."

Jamie looked across a couple of fairways and a river, his eye resting on the clubhouse in the distance. "Sure," he stammered, "I didn't mean to—"

"Forget it," Al said. "One other thing."

"Yes?"

"Does this web site of yours run banner ads?"

"That's the plan in the long run. Nothing yet."

"Can you run one for me, gratis?"

"What would it say?"

"You're the writer. Something like 'Far East Electronica for all your audio/video needs. Only cheaper'."

"Sure, I could do that. Once other advertisers see it, they'll figure you're paying and I could charge the next one who comes along."

Al smiled broadly. "Win/win." Then, cribbing a phrase the Beatles used to ask themselves in their salad days, Al asked, "Where we goin', Johnny?"

On cue, Jamie returned the smile and said in his best Scouser accent: "To the toppermost of the poppermost."

■ ■ ■

The day they paid off the debt on their last credit card, Jamie and Sheena decided to celebrate by taking Theo and Ariana to the revolving restaurant overlooking the lake high above the city.

It had taken three long years to cut the plastic habit, and Jamie intended to pay cash for the celebration. Luckily the whole city was in the midst of a summer promotion and even the best restaurants had reasonably priced prix-fixe gourmet selections well within the budget of Froogers like themselves.

As she ran out to work that morning, Sheena assured him she would join them at the restaurant after running a few errands late in the afternoon. Jamie wondered what errands couldn't wait another day, but agreed they could arrive separately. When Theo and Ariana joined Jamie at the restaurant, Sheena still hadn't arrived.

"Great view," Theo began. "I haven't been here since they built this in the mid 70s."

It was early evening and some cloud cover obscured the setting sun. The view of the lake made Jamie think of Victor in Rochester. He really needed to connect with his brother again soon.

"I love the lake," said Jamie. "One day we'll buy a cottage with a lake view. Sheena's always arguing with her brother Eamon about scheduling summer vacation at her mother's cottage."

"Who doesn't want a retreat by the lake?" Theo said.

"That's the problem with you retiring baby boomers. You all want the same things at the same time and drive up prices."

Theo shrugged. "If you can live without a lake, you can get a lot more vacation property for your dollar." He glanced lovingly at Ariana, who had been studying the menu. "Isn't that right, honey?"

Ariana smiled, setting aside the menu and rejoining the conversation. "That's right, darling. One day you'll have to visit our cottage, Jamie. I'm afraid it's not on a lake, but we have much more property for quite a bit less money. That's one argument I don't mind having lost." She patted Theo's hand gently.

"Any place to escape the city would be fine by me," Jamie said, perusing the menu.

"Surely recreational property isn't your priority right now? Still renting that condo?"

"We can dream, can't we? We may be close to a deal with our landlords. I've been putting aside the money Al's been paying me for helping out with his new business."

"Your friend the electronics importer? Isn't he your poker buddy?"

"Not so much these days. We're both so busy. How's your bridge coming?"

Theo's eyes lit up and he said with a grin, "Now there's a wonderful game. I play mostly online. When I'm dummy and get to sit out the hand, I often drop in on Vinyl Nation."

"So that's why you stay only five minutes."

"Guilty. But you must admit I've given you some good pointers during those chats, tips the whole community benefits from."

"The whole site seems almost as keen on our financial discussions as they are about vinyl." Jamie glanced anxiously towards the door, looking for Sheena.

"How much do you think you can buy the condo for?" Ariana asked.

"Rob and Janice are practically friends, so we can bypass the realtors and pocket the 6% commission we'd otherwise have to pay. We're splitting the difference. They said they'd let it go for $285,000."

"Sheena must be ecstatic."

"She is. Same place, but it will be a totally different feeling owning it instead of paying rent forever."

"Home ownership is the only way to go," Theo said, "How are the other pieces of your financial plan going?"

"Making progress. I already told you the reason for this celebration. Didi was right. Finally guerrilla frugality is starting to pay off. But it was really tough for Sheena. It was only when I told her it was a war, us against them, that she really started to buy in to being a Frooger."

Theo nodded in approval. "Eliminating credit-card debt is a huge milestone. Congratulations on getting that monkey off your back in only three years. Let me order a good wine. Our treat."

Theo beckoned the wine waiter, who had been politely hovering. He pointed to a vintage bottle that met with an approving nod.

"So now you only have Sheena's student loan, and that's at a reasonably low interest rate. Well done."

"Bernie's been doing a great job for us."

"How much did he charge you for the financial plan?"

"*Comprehensive* financial plan," Jamie smiled, "$1,000. Of course, we'd rather work with you."

"You're in good hands with Bernie. You know he owns the whole building that houses the Vinyl Cave?"

"He mentioned that. He lives with his cats in an apartment above the store and rents out the other two units. I guess that's why Sheena keeps asking him about real estate as an investment."

"It's certainly a major component of a diversified financial plan," Theo said, "but you still haven't put in place the foundation: your own paid-up home."

"Maybe we should buy a duplex, live in one and rent out the other."

"Not a bad idea if you can live in that much space. Of course, being a landlord has its downsides. There are other ways to skin the real estate cat."

"Such as?"

The waiter opened a bottle, poured a bit in Theo's glass and let him take a sniff. Theo approved and the waiter went through his pouring routine.

"Such as REITs."

"Mutual funds?"

"Sort of. You can buy real estate mutual funds or you can buy individual Real Estate Investment Trusts or REITs. Or you can buy a whole basket of REITs through an exchange-traded fund."

"Less of a hassle than being woken up by tenants at three in the morning to unplug their toilets."

"You've got that right," Theo grinned, "which is why some of my clients put 10% of their portfolios into REITs. Some, however, are like Sheena and prefer the reality of bricks, mortar and land. Speaking of which, where is your child bride?"

As Rochester came back into view, Jamie glanced at the digital time on his cell phone. "Should be here any moment. Some important appointments after school that wouldn't keep."

"Speak of the devil," Theo waved a hand towards the entrance. "Sheena, you're just in time for a good glass of wine."

Sheena appeared flustered, almost breathless. "Sorry I was late. Crazy afternoon. I'll just have water for now," she added, putting her hand on the glass just as Theo proffered the wine bottle.

"Not a problem," Theo said. "Jamie was just telling us the good news about the condo."

"Good news?" Sheena said, as she slipped the linen serviette into her lap.

"Yes, that your landlords have agreed to sell at what seems a very fair price." Sheena looked at Theo as if he were speaking Greek and she didn't understand a word.

"Honey," she grabbed Jamie's hand. "We need to talk."

"Talk away. We're among friends."

"Privately," she urged.

"Nonsense. Theo and Ariana know everything there is to know about our lives, and not just our finances."

Jamie took another sip of wine, then continued. "Matter of fact, most of Vinyl Nation knows all about our plans for financial independence."

"Jamie!"

He ignored her unspoken plea. "'Fess up babe. What's your big news?"

"Very well then, Theo, Ariana."

"Yes, honey," Ariana said, touching her hand.

"I don't think we can buy the condo after all."

"Why not?" Jamie asked, a frown marking his forehead. "We just cut a great deal for the place."

Sheena drew a deep breath. Squeezing Jamie's hand she blurted, "Because we're pregnant."

"Wonderful news," Ariana hugged Sheena, while Theo pattered her fondly on the back.

Dumfounded, Jamie just stared for a second before he jumped up to hug his teary-eyed wife. "How? When?" he sputtered, stepping back to look into those shining green eyes he loved so much.

"I think you know the how, darling," she replied with a blush. "And the when is just over six months from now."

"So what's the problem with the condo? It's perfect timing. We'll decorate the spare bedroom."

"There's not going to be enough room," Sheena said, sitting down and looking at her husband. "I think we should buy a detached home with a yard."

"Sure, we'll do that one day, but the condo will do for now. Hey," he grabbed her hand again, "do you know if it's a boy or a girl?"

Sheena sighed with exasperation. "Both. That's what I've been trying to tell you. We're pregnant with twins, one of each."

Chapter 6

Teach Your Children

[CROSBY, STILLS, NASH & YOUNG, 1970]

"Twins?" Jamie stammered, "As in two of them?"

"That's right, darling," Sheena said, barely audibly. She reached across the restaurant table, curled her fingers around his and added, "Our son and daughter."

"I didn't even know that was possible," Jamie said. "Aren't twins always the same sex?"

"They are if they're from one egg. But ours are fraternal or dizygotic, which means two separate eggs. They're the most common type of twins."

"I see," said Jamie, recovering his composure. He wiped his brow with his napkin and took a deep slug of water. "So we'll have the perfect family right out the gate." Making eye contact with Theo, he added: "A stock and a bond."

"A balanced fund," laughed Theo, and everyone joined in.

"You're right about the space issue," Jamie said. "It was going to be tight with just one child. You *are* sure about this, aren't you?"

"Would you like to see the Ultra Sound?"

"Sure."

She dug the diagnostic image out of her purse. "There's number one," she pointed. "And there's number two." They stared, mesmerized. Jamie held the paper in his shaking hands.

"Which is which?"

"Who can tell at this stage?" Sheena had already examined every detail of the amazing sight.

"Two of them ... You're right. This puts a crimp in the idea of buying the condo."

"I know. Rob will be disappointed. But Janice will be thrilled for us."

"I'm thrilled too," Jamie said, although his mind was churning. No more late nights playing poker with Al and the boys, he thought: Time to get serious about life.

Then aloud, "When is the great event?"

"I told you. Six and a half months. Mid-January, I'd guess."

Jamie thought back to that glorious spring day a few months earlier. "Now I remember the 'how' ... Still, that gives us time to find a larger condo."

"I was thinking a real detached home in the 'burbs," Sheena said. "They'll need plenty of space in the outdoors. You can't have dogs cooped up inside a small apartment."

"Dogs?" Jamie said. *What am I getting myself into?*

"Sure, children need pets."

"How about cats? Bernie has a couple of Siamese I'm sure he'd like to donate to the cause."

"Let's cross that bridge when we get to it," said Sheena.

Jamie couldn't help himself as he started to consider the financial side of this announcement. *I may have to push back Findependence Day a few years.* Then, to Theo, "Are children tax-deductible?"

There was a pause as the two women looked at each other as if Jamie were from Mars. Then Jamie laughed along with Theo, as he realized how ridiculous he sounded.

"As it happens, there are some tax breaks associated with children," Theo said. "But Sheena's right. You don't have to worry about it right away. There are of course additional expenses as well."

"No kidding," Jamie said. "I read it costs $100,000 to raise a child. So we're looking at 200 grand here, minimum."

"That's conservative," Ariana said. "You don't raise a family in order to save money. How about an aperitif?" She flagged down the waiter and they ordered liqueurs all round with a bottle of Perrier for the expectant mom.

"It depends on what choices you want to make for their education," Theo broke in. "You could spend that much just on private school."

"The public system worked perfectly fine for Jamie and me," Sheena said. "Seems to me private school is a waste of money, and the children just end up snobs."

"I don't know about that," Theo said. "I went to one. Do you consider me a snob?"

"You went to private school?" Sheena said. "You're the exception to the rule."

"It's a great place to meet people who may become friends for life," Theo said, "or people who may become important business or political connections. I don't consider education to be an expense: it's an investment—back to our human capital view of the world."

"I don't get you," Jamie said. The waiter had just served him some Zambuca, and he was entranced by the blue flames engulfing the beans.

"Remember I said you're richer than you think because of your future earning power?"

"Sure."

"Well," Theo said, pointing across the table to Sheena's belly, "for these two, there's nothing but future earning power. Maybe $5-million worth over the course of their entire lives. Or more."

"If they're anything like the Olsen twins," Sheena quipped. Theo grinned. "So don't begrudge whatever you spend educating these two," he said. "It's an investment that will eventually pay dividends."

"I wouldn't have thought about it that way, but I suppose you're right," said Jamie. "But first things first. We have to tell Janice and Rob, and then I guess we're going to have to bite the bullet and work with a real estate agent to find a home."

"With a back yard," Ariana added.

"With a back yard," Jamie agreed. "With plenty of space for the cats."

■ ■ ■

A few weeks later, Al strolled through the doors of Tech Heaven. It was near lunchtime, and he found Jamie directing two recent hires about sales techniques. All he could make out were the words "extended warranty," but he could guess the rest.

"Jamie," he called, "when you're finished with these killer sales guys, can I have a quick word?"

"Sure, Al, Give me a minute. Meet me in the Surround Sound Room."

Al walked past the computer section and the wide-screen TVs to enter the audio-visual show room. He muted the console, whipped out his Blackberry and focused on dealing with business. He was nearly done when Jamie joined him.

"What's new, friend?" Al asked, thumbing for a few more seconds.

"Really want to know?"

Jamie's tone of voice caused Al to look up. "Sure."

"I'm going to be a father. Twice over."

Al glanced back down at his machine but said nothing.

"Sheena's going to have twins, a boy and a girl. We start house-hunting tomorrow."

"Great news," Al said, still thumbing his Blackberry. "Nothing like fatherhood to make a man out of you."

Jamie nodded. "Now I've gotten over the double whammy, I'm looking forward to it."

"Can I ask you a question?"

"Shoot."

"Better shut the door."

Jamie did so, and Al raised the volume on the stereo in the room to block the conversation from prying ears. He pulled out an envelope from his jacket and handed it to Jamie. It contained a cheque that Jamie stuffed into his pocket.

"Thanks, man."

"You did a great job on the last set of brochures," Al said, "but it's not as effective as publicity."

"Publicity?" Jamie asked, his eyes narrowing. "I'm not a press agent."

"No, but you're a writer, and you know other writers and editors in the trade press."

"Sure. Vinyl Nation has come in handy that way."

"So when you're writing up the copy for some of these brochures, why not go the extra mile?" Al asked. "Pull a few favors and get your editor friends to write them up in the audio and video rags."

Jamie's face betrayed no emotion. "They'd have to be newsworthy."

"Sure, but sometimes these editors need to be reminded about what's news. My suppliers would be grateful for the exposure if you catch my drift, squire." Al knew Jamie loved Monty Python.

Al patted his pocket. "You could pay down a lot more debt that way." He began to open the door to leave but then closed it again.

"One more thing, Jamie. I'd really appreciate it if you could give these little guys a helping hand." Al opened his briefcase to reveal a new line of accessories.

"We're having a special promotion on the filters. The top salesperson in each district wins a free trip to Shenzhen. I'd love you to move these up top and promote the wheels off them."

"I'd have to clear that with Jharhid."

"Sure. Tell him he can qualify too. Here's the literature. It's all explained there. You wrote it, after all."

Al left the A/V room with Jamie following a step behind. Back on the main floor, Al turned towards the shelves indicating two new products. "These should be at the end of the aisle. Get the guys to hustle them."

Jamie raised one eyebrow but did not reply.

"I know they're crud," Al continued. "Here's the thing. The profit margin is through the roof, and you can make bonus commissions—a little extra that Jharhid and the taxman don't need to know about."

From the expression on Jamie's face, Al knew he wasn't going for it, not yet anyway. After a longer pause than was comfortable, Jamie said, "I'll have to—"

Al frowned, but then said cheerfully, "I know, you'll have to check with the J-Man. Let me know what he says."

Jamie nodded, looking around nervously in case his boss or other salespeople were within earshot.

"Free for poker tonight?" Al asked.

"Not with the jerks who groped my wife," scowled Jamie.

Remembering the incident, Al shrugged. "They were just into the juice. Harmless enough. Just a friendly game with potential investors. Think you'll have time to have fun once those twins arrive? Better yet, drop by the hotel bar beforehand. There are a couple of new waitresses I'd like to introduce you to."

■ ■ ■

Their landlords were disappointed, but as Sheena predicted, Janice was thrilled by the news of the pregnancy. "No way you could raise twins here," she said, when she dropped by the apartment to pick up the next rent cheque. "Tell you the truth, I wasn't sure you could raise even one child here, but I couldn't tell Rob that. He was counting on the sale to raise money for another investment property he has his eye on. No big deal."

"That's a relief," Sheena said. "Want some tea?"

Janice shook her head as she sat down at the kitchen table. Sheena put the kettle on anyway. She looked around the condo. "You have, what, 1,200 square feet here?"

From the living room, Jamie looked up from his newspaper. When it came to real estate, Janice was an expert. "I was thinking 2,000 square feet would be okay, downtown somewhere, close to work and transit," Jamie yelled.

"That's so not on," Sheena replied. "Not enough space, not enough yard and too much mixed neighbourhood. This city isn't as safe as it used to be. Seems there's a shooting every week."

Jamie got up from the couch and pulled up one of the kitchen chairs.

"Figure 800 square feet more for each of the twins and you want a minimum 3,000," Janice said.

"I was chatting about this with Theo on the site," Jamie said. "He pointed out that if we buy downtown we could ditch one of the cars. That alone would save $10,000 a year in payments, upkeep and insurance."

"He has a point," Janice added. "But so does Sheena. Are you sure you want to raise twins downtown?"

"I'm sure we don't," Sheena said. "I've asked Rhonda—the realtor you recommended, thanks very much—to scout out some properties in the suburbs."

"New or resale?" asked Janice.

"Preferably new, even though they'll tack on sales tax. I was thinking of something like the new Apple Blossoms Estates they're building up by the escarpment."

The kettle was whistling. Sheena put two tea bags in the teapot and poured the water.

Janice raised her eyebrows. "Apple Blossoms? Nice area but no bargain. Look, guys, I've got to scoot. Thanks for the cheque. I guess we won't be getting many more of these from you."

As soon as she was gone, Jamie turned angrily to Sheena. "Apple Blossoms Estates? Have you lost your mind?"

"We can afford it," Sheena said defensively. "I ran the numbers."

Calmly, she poured the tea.

"Since when are you a numbers person? Who ran the numbers for you?"

"The mortgage guy at the bank."

"What did he say?"

"He said we could afford a brand new 3,000-square-foot home as long as we stay out of the downtown core and major transit stops."

"In other words, the boonies. What does he mean by 'afford'?" Jamie sipped his tea but was hardly conscious of it.

"Afford. You know. Low monthly payments so we have plenty of cash left for other things."

"How low?"

"$1,350 a month. Carries like rent, he said."

"For how long?"

"35 years but—"

"35 years?" Jamie exploded, "Did you not hear a single word Theo said about getting a house you can afford and paying it off in a few years?"

He walked to the living room and slapped a piece of vinyl on the turntable, some innocuous New Age music Bernie had recommended.

"I always listen to what Theo has to say, but that was just a theoretical discussion," Sheena said. "We have real babies on the way and all kinds of other expenses. It would just be for a few years while we get established."

She went to the kitchen pantry, grabbed a bag of chocolate cookies and threw them on the table. "Help yourself."

Jamie tore the bag open and retrieved two cookies. "Then what? Just as we're putting aside a few bucks, you'll want to fill the giant yard with a pool and a tennis court?"

"A pool would be nice."

"Or a garage and heated driveway?"

"You don't have to get sarcastic."

"Which reminds me. If we wind up in a place like Apple Blossoms, I'm looking at a 100-mile commute every day. That's 500 miles every week."

"You enjoy driving."

"Have you checked the price of gas lately? Know how much the old Firebird will chew up on that commute? Assuming it lasts much longer."

"Take public transit like other Froogers. A bus connects Apple Blossoms with the subway. Think of the reading you could get done."

"I need a car for business. We'd have to buy a new car and a fuel-efficient one at that. But it's not in the plan."

"What plan?"

"The one Bernie drew up. You know, the guy from the Vinyl Cave."

She made a face.

"Oh, him."

"Yeah, him. He may be an old hippie who's into vinyl, but he's also a CFP."

"CFP?"

She munched another cookie, pushing the bag to him, but he declined.

"Certified Financial Planner. He knows his stuff."

"Then he can find a way for us to buy a new car. You can't have that old muscle car sitting on the driveway of a new home in Apple Blossoms."

"I know. Jharhid has family that lives there. The only cars there are Beemers, Lexuses and Mercedes, he told me."

"We have to keep up appearances."

"Appearances can be deceiving. Remember Al's mansion?"

"Sure. It's gorgeous."

"I don't think he has $20,000 of equity in that place. The more I work with him, the more I wonder just how much he does have. He keeps asking me to invest some money in his business. Equity costs, he keeps saying."

"Have you?"

She looked concerned, twisting her wedding ring.

"Are you kidding? With what? The point is it's costly trying to keep up with the Joneses in expensive neighbourhoods. I'd rather be in a less ostentatious part of town."

"On the wrong side of the tracks, you mean," Sheena said.

"I'm talking about reasonably sized houses in respectable neighbourhoods even if they're not what you'd consider tony. Like the homes owned by the people in *The Millionaire Next Door*[3]."

Sheena suppressed a yawn. "Is that another of those money books Theo keeps lending you?"

"Yes, but the point is people like Al and the yuppies living in the palatial homes of Apple Blossoms are in all likelihood examples of Big Hat, No Cattle."

"I've heard the expression."

"The true millionaires live in regular homes and drive modest cars they keep on the road a long time. One of the richest men in the world still lives in the home he bought when he first got married—Warren Buffett. Anyone who looked at the house from the outside would have no idea how much wealth lurked behind those walls."

"What's the point of being rich if it's invisible?"

"The point is that with enough financial assets, you have freedom."

She sighed, getting exasperated.

"Financial independence, I know."

"How many times do I have to spell it out for you?" Jamie said, getting frustrated. "If you spend like a millionaire, you'll end up a pauper. Spend like a pauper, and you have a shot at becoming a millionaire. That's why we're Froogers."

"I don't know about that. Look at Al. He dresses nicely, drives a fancy car and lives in a mansion. Look at all the business deals that come his way as a result. People want to do business with people who appear to be a success."

"Appear being the operative word."

"Big hat, no cattle?"

Jamie grinned.

"Which is another reason you want to move to Apple Blossoms," Sheena said.

"I don't follow."

"You'll need a big yard to put all your cattle!"

Jamie had to laugh. "I may need to ride one of them to work, but if this is so important to you, we can look."

"So we can get a new house in the suburbs?"

"I don't know how we can afford it and still keep on track for Findependence Day, but we'll find a way."

"Thank you, honey." Sheena flung her arms around him. Then, she whispered in his ear, "You'll love it. I promise."

[3]See appendix, A Peek at Theo's Library

Chapter 7

Our House

[CSN&Y, 1970; MADNESS, 1982]

The perfect, affordable house was an elusive commodity. Sheena dragged Jamie through more than 50 prospects, and it took three months to locate it. To placate Jamie, Sheena went through the motions of viewing a few downtown properties, but quickly spotted the obvious drawbacks of any house that Jamie found appealing. Taking her cue from the dominant decision-maker on the domestic front, Rhonda the agent sided with Sheena.

Jamie was irked that reasonable prices did not seem to enter the equation for Rhonda. He knew that the higher the price tag, the bigger her commission, but he didn't want to accuse her openly of a conflict of interest. He noticed, too, that Rhonda had a knack for damning with faint praise.

"It's charming, I'll grant you, but did you see the size of the kitchen? I've seen bigger ones on sailboats." Or, if the house itself was up to muster, "Very nice, but did you notice the slum across the street? I'm sure it's a crack house. You don't want the twins exposed to those needles."

So Apple Blossoms Estates it was: 38 Verdant Crescent, priced to within $1,000 of Jamie's theoretical maximum. At 3,000 square feet, it was the smallest model in the exclusive enclave. It was tucked away on a big back corner lot with just enough trees to merit the description of verdant.

Sheena was ecstatic. Even Jamie had to admit the community would be the perfect place to raise a growing family. The house itself seemed ideal. The smallest rooms dwarfed the biggest ones in the condo. The entrance foyer wasn't on the same scale as Al's mansion, but Jamie had to admit it was impressive, particularly with the light flooding in from the skylight.

Before the moving van was out of the driveway, Sheena noted how shabby their old furniture appeared against the spanking new white walls of the living room.

"They'll have to go," was her opening salvo.

"We can't aff—" Jamie began but was cut off.

"Sure we can. Now we have home equity we can get a line of credit."

"Equity? We only put 5% down, despite Theo's warning against high-ratio mortgages."

"No thanks to you did we come up with that much. If my mother hadn't come through, I don't know where we'd be."

"Solvent." Jamie started setting up his audio gear in the den, a cozy sunken room with an old-fashioned fireplace. Sheena had set up shop in the adjacent kitchen, unpacking china and other culinary essentials.

"Don't fret. Would you prefer La-Z-boy or Leon's?"

"Furniture? Whatever's cheaper."

"Always with the Frooger routine. Normal people don't worry so much about spending. What about the extra money Al's been paying you?"

"That's business income. I put the cheques into Vinyl Nation Enterprises Inc. That's why we incorporated, remember? Depending on the storage and office space I use, we might be able to deduct 15% of our household expenses against that income."

Sheena's face lit up. "So we can expense new furniture and drapes for the den and for the office upstairs? That's great."

"Depends what the accountant says. Now we have all this space, I'd like to set aside part of the basement to house Vinyl Nation." Jamie nodded in the direction of a large clump of boxes full of old LPs.

"You'd bring back those old records from Al's place?"

"Sure. You can't object to that."

"The less you have to do with that man, the better. Just don't start spreading on to the main floors."

"Before you go crazy with new appliances and furniture, don't forget we have to buy a new car."

"Pity," she said, still fussing with the curtains. She peered beyond into the driveway. From the look on her face, Jamie figured she was unhappy about what their new neighbours would think about their two cars.

"The Firebird should last another fifty thousand clicks," Sheena said. "Couldn't you drive my Corolla sometimes?"

That was *her* car, bought after she landed her first steady teaching gig. Once she went on maternity leave, he could take it to work. The Firebird was a gas-guzzler. With prices at the pump soaring, Bernie's plan called for him to take the train at least every other day. Besides, the Firebird wasn't exactly a family car. Unsuccessfully, Jamie tried to picture dual car seats in the back of his 'bird.

He lugged a box into the kitchen where Sheena was sorting plates and cutlery.

"How about we lease one?" he suggested.

She brightened. "That way we'd always have a nice late-model car and wouldn't have to deal with repair costs once the warranties expired."

"Problem is, leasing is like renting an apartment," said Jamie. "It never ends. The last five years the Firebird has hardly cost us anything."

She whirled around to face him, still clutching two plates.

"Did you forget about the $800 brake repair last year? Or the $1,100 AC bill last summer? Running old cars into the ground isn't the bargain everyone thinks it is, and they're terrible for the environment."

"It's a gamble. But think of the months when everything is fine and there are no payments. With a lease you're looking at $200 or $300 a month, month in and month out, with no let-up. I'd rather own and take my chances on how long it lasts."

"But at least there are no unexpected additional expenses when you lease," Sheena said. "Besides, if you stick with Tech Heaven you're going to keep getting raises. Your human capital is rising all the time."

He'd opened a box of kitchen appliances but had no clue where to put them. Sheena gave him an exasperated look, grabbed a few items and put them in their proper spots.

"I thought you never listened to Theo's financial planning lessons?"

"I like the human capital idea. See, Jamie, we're richer than you think. But until you start converting your human capital into cold hard cash, you can be a good little Frooger and take transit half the time. We have higher priorities. Try it a few months and see how you like it."

Jamie hated it when Sheena used Theo's lessons against him.

■ ■ ■

Outside the maternity ward, Jamie paced back and forth. Sheena was three weeks ahead of schedule, not surprising given the double blessings being bestowed upon them. When she'd woken him up at 5:30 that morning, Jamie was so excited he'd blasted out an announcement to everyone on the Vinyl Nation site before leaving for the hospital.

"Hey, Jamie."

Jamie stopped pacing and spun around at the sound of the familiar voice. "Theo! What are you doing here?" He grabbed his friend's hand, shaking it and clapping him on the back at the same time.

As usual, Theo was dressed immaculately, sporting a dark suit and maroon silk tie.

"This is a huge day in your life."

"Huge alright. At least Sheena is."

"No turning back now. When I read your post I thought you might like some company for the wait. One advantage of financial independence is you have time for this sort of thing."

"They just kicked me out a minute ago. I'm glad for the company."

"I won't be able to stick around for the main event," Theo glanced at his watch. "I have a meeting 20 blocks from here in an hour. But you'll be busy with Sheena and babies then anyway. The waiting is the hardest part for us dads."

The two men settled into the teal vinyl settees, typical of hospital waiting rooms everywhere. Theo waved his hand in the direction of a plastic display case sitting on top of an adjoining side table. "Have you read the brochure yet?"

Jamie blinked. "Brochure?"

Theo grabbed a brochure from the display case and handed it to Jamie. The cover featured the picture of an adorable baby.

"You can't visit a maternity ward without seeing one of these: A savings plan for your children. Registered Education Savings Plans, or RESPs."

"They haven't even been born yet, and someone's trying to sell them something?"

"Remember human capital? Education is an investment."

"Sheena uses that against me whenever it's convenient."

"Smart woman. Perhaps I should take her on as a client before you."

"Not the way she spends. I'm not sure we'll ever accumulate the $250,000 you insist upon."

"No rush. But I do think you should enrol the twins in this." He waved the brochure.

"What's the deal?"

"Again, free money from the government."

Theo got up from the couch. As he launched into a lecture, Jamie thought Theo had missed his calling as a university professor. "Like your retirement savings plan, but instead of an upfront tax deduction they give you a grant."

Theo paused, fixing Jamie with an "I hope you're listening" stare. Then he continued. "Almost as enticing is the fact that all the investment income generated inside the plan is tax-free until the students need to spend it. Then they withdraw the money, hopefully with minimum taxes. That part of it is similar to the 529 College Savings Plans in many American states."

"Yes, but Victor says only half the states offer tax deductions on them. How much is the grant from the Canadian government?"

"20% of the first $2,500 a year per child. I'd recommend you commit to $5,000 a year for the pair of them, which would generate a combined education savings grant of $1,000 each year to a maximum of $7,200 per child.

Jamie whistled. "That would cost us more than $400 a month." He walked over to the window and gazed out at a small park adjoining the parking lot.

"It's the only way to go. With your finances, you'd never come up with a lump sum of $5,000 every year."

"Don't I know it."

"Set up a family or multi-beneficiary plan, which will give you more flexibility if only one child decides to pursue higher education. Arrange with a mutual fund provider for a preauthorized debit of $416/month and forget about it."

"Mutual funds?"

"A mutual fund RESP, yes. If a lump sum, I'd suggest a balanced fund or a straight equity fund if you're making monthly payments consistently."

"I thought you didn't like mutual fund fees."

"I don't for most of my wealthy clients, but for this kind of investment—small monthly payments—I don't think you can beat the diversification and convenience of mutual funds."

"What happened to exchange-traded funds?"

Theo nodded in approval.

"Once the accounts grow to, say, $20,000 you could switch to self-directed plans and buy ETFs or stocks and bonds directly. By the time the twins are ready for college 18 years from now, you could have $100,000 for them plus any growth. What better way to unleash their human capital?"

Jamie grinned and thumbed through the brochure. "It doesn't say anything about mutual funds here."

"No, that's a pooled scholarship plan."

"Which is?"

"Much the same thing but it invests only in fixed income. They also have hefty upfront fixed sales charges. Your twins have a long enough time horizon that they can afford to take some risk and get equity exposure, so a mutual fund would be better for them."

"They'll be richer than me if I don't start saving that much myself."

"Jamie, Jamie, Jamie." Theo looked fondly at the younger man. "Financial independence is a marathon, not a sprint. Speaking of which, why don't we stretch our legs?"

"I'm not so sure about getting rich slowly," Jamie said as they walked down the hospital corridor. The pungent anaesthetic odor of hospitals everywhere was stronger here than in the waiting room. "I'm with Al on this one: make the big score on a couple of hyper-growth stocks. All you need to find is one Microsoft in 1986 or Apple in 2000."

Theo considered this, lightly biting his lower lip.

"Or Nortel or Enron or Bre-X. It cuts both ways."

"I like to swing for the fences. Mutual funds are like hitting singles. Bonds are like being walked."

"Babe Ruth wasn't just famous for his home runs. He also had a spectacular number of strikeouts."

Jamie wasn't sure he should raise the subject but decided to chance it. "Between you and me, Al gave me a tip on a Chinese electronics stock that's about to soar."

"How do you know that?"

"They're about to ink a big deal with Wal-Mart. It's going to the moon."

Theo didn't look impressed. He stopped walking and faced Jamie directly. "If you've got inside information, you can't trade on it. The securities commissions will come down on you hard. And if it's public information, the market already knows about it, and it's fairly priced."

"I know about the efficient market. I finished reading that book you lent me: *Unconventional Success*[1]. I'm just not sure I believe it."

Theo's brow furrowed.

"Unless you plan to become a professional money manager, there's no point trying to beat the pros at their own game. You're up against people who got their MBAs at Wharton and studied for years to become Chartered Financial Analysts. You're competing with seasoned mutual fund managers, pension funds and young hedge fund stars. They have computer systems and proprietary research that even I can't

[1] See appendix, A Peek at Theo's Library

afford. Think you know something they don't know?"

"So I may as well buy mutual funds and let the pros do it for me?"

"Better than trying it yourself and getting your head handed to you." Theo increased his pace, deep in thought. "The problem is investing is a zero-sum game, and the pros on average can't even beat the indexes. Subtract the cost of their own fees, plus brokerage commissions, taxes and other things, and it's mighty hard for them to beat index funds or ETFs."

"If I were happy settling for market returns, I'd accept the argument for indexing," Jamie said, "But I want to wrestle the market to the ground and wring its scrawny neck."

Theo laughed. "I saw the same advertisement. Maybe one in a hundred can succeed at it."

They'd reached the end of the corridor. Through a locked glass door, Jamie could see the maternity ward. He buzzed it and a nurse popped her head through the door.

"I'm Sheena Morelli's husband," he said. "May I see her?"

The nurse shook her head. "Not just now. We're at a critical stage. We'll call you when it's time to move her to delivery."

"When's that?"

She looked at her watch. "I'd say about ten minutes."

Jamie nodded and they retraced their steps down the corridor.

"Now I'm getting nervous."

"Don't be," Theo said. "They know what they're doing. It can't be easy for them with twins and a nervous husband hanging around."

"I'll cool it," Jamie agreed. After a few seconds of silence he asked: "How about private equity? If Al ever gets Far East Electronica to the next level, I'd be in on the ground floor. I'd control my own destiny."

"Might happen. Might not. You seem to have taken this 'I'm a stock' thing to heart." Theo seemed more relaxed. "How's Vinyl Nation going? There appear to be more participants every day."

"It's alright. I got my accountant to incorporate it. But you may be right about it being just a hobby business. I couldn't even fund the twins' education plans from the few records I'm mailing out."

"Anything worth building takes time."

"The rate I'm going, Findependence Day will happen the day I turn 65, just like everyone else. Victor is resigned to waiting till 67, when Social Security kicks in."

"Your brother's fortunate. America's government pensions are more generous than Canada's, assuming Uncle Sam stays solvent enough to make good on the promise."

"Maybe we should move down there before the twins start to grow roots."

"Then you lose the healthcare system in this country."

They reached a vending machine. Jamie dropped in some change for coffee and asked Theo if he wanted one.

"It's all a trade-off," Theo said, shaking his head to decline Jamie's offer. "I assume you've seen Michael Moore's 'Sicko'?"

"I loved the scene where the sick Americans were loaded on to a boat to Cuba to get treatment. A scathing indictment. Too bad Bill and Hillary couldn't take on the insurance companies when they were in power."

"Which reminds me. Have you talked to your insurance agent about life insurance?"

"Another expense," Jamie said as they walked back to the waiting room. Jamie took a sip of his coffee and made a face. "When does it end?"

"You don't know the half of it. Right now, what would you say your biggest asset is?"

"I know what you're going to say: it's still my future earning power."

"Right. And what happens if you suddenly die when the twins are just a year or two old?"

"Then Sheena is in a tight situation. No way she could carry that house and pay for daycare on her salary."

"Right again. If all goes well, you live to a ripe old age and gradually convert all that human capital into financial capital. When you reach Findependence Day, you won't need much life insurance. The twins will be in college or married."

Jamie stopped in mid-sip. He'd never thought much beyond the baby stage. The thought of grown-up children was even scarier.

"But," Theo continued, "if, God forbid, you made an early departure from the planet, you'd never have the chance to realize that human capital. Life insurance would be there to provide instant financial capital in case the worst happened."

"So on top of starting an education savings plan we need to buy some life insurance." Jamie took another sip of coffee and made a face. "Let's get the insurance now," he said. "This coffee could kill me."

Theo smiled. After a moment, Jamie continued. "With all those expenses, that doesn't leave much room for a stock portfolio?"

"Doesn't sound like it, apart from whatever stocks you own in your pension plan. That's a start."

"You were right about the workplace pension deductions being painless. When they come right off my paycheque, I barely notice the pension contributions."

A nurse popped her head into the waiting room.

"Is there a Mr. Morelli here?"

Theo got up from the couch and smiled. "Game on."

■ ■ ■

They named their son after Jamie's Italian grandfather: Marcello. They named their daughter after Sheena's Irish grandmother: Michaela. Life was chaos.

Amid the turmoil of the first weeks after the twins' arrival in mid-January, only the education savings plans got started, and then only because Theo got the ball rolling by seeding the initial contribution. His christening gift of $500 each opened their plans when the minor Morellis were three months old.

As the weeks passed, Jamie boned up on life insurance whenever he could spare two minutes from working, feeding or changing the twins. He hoped there was a way to combine life insurance with the investing program he was so anxious to begin.

"With whole life or permanent insurance, not only can we protect our human capital, but we can also end up with a pot of investment money at the end of it," he told Sheena over the breakfast table one Saturday morning. "The best of both worlds."

"Aren't the premiums a lot higher? Can we afford more than barebones insurance?"

"I don't know. Why don't we ask Theo?" Jamie walked into the den and powered up his laptop. Theo wasn't on the Vinyl Nation site, however. Jamie tried one of Theo's online bridge sites and found Theo playing under one of his favourite handles. Jamie signed on and kibitzed while Theo played a hand.

When he was dummy, Jamie greeted his friend through the accompanying chat site. "Greetings, stranger. You're dummy, right, so I can chat for a few moments?"

"You're catching on," Theo typed back. "Are you ready to take your first bridge lesson?"

"First things first," Jamie typed, "Remember that day in the maternity ward and our chat about life insurance?"

"Sure. I'm not as fast a typist as you. I'll phone you."

Jamie picked up on the second ring. "Where was I?" Theo said. "Oh yes, when the twins were delivered I suggested you buy basic term insurance and keep the policy in force at least until they grow up."

"My insurance agent doesn't think term is a great idea."

"He wouldn't. He makes more money selling you permanent insurance or a Universal Life policy."

"That's it. He said something about UL and how it will provide tax-efficient growth in the market as well as insurance coverage for my family. Sounds perfect."

"Perfect except the premiums are much higher. I don't think it's a good idea to mix insurance with investing, at least not while you're still trying to eliminate debt."

"Why not?"

Jamie shoved aside the piles of tiny baby laundry, neatly folded and stacked, so he could make room for the next basket Sheena delivered, still warm from the dryer.

"For one, there's the same fee problem with permanent insurance as when you invest in mutual funds or wrap programs directly. Not many of them I know are invested in index funds."

"So?"

"Remember, costs matter. If mutual fund Management Expense Ratios or MERs are running between 2% and 3% a year, they'll cut your investment returns by 20% or 30% over three or four decades. Wrap programs and insurance segregated funds also have hefty MERs, so you need to shop around for the ones with lower fees."

"Not always easy, right?"

"Right. But more importantly, remember what this is for. To protect your human capital in case the worst happens."

"But the agent told me term is like renting: money out the door with no return at the end."

"He's right. You didn't begrudge the rent money when you and Sheena first got married, did you?"

"No, but we knew we wouldn't be renting forever."

"You won't have to pay insurance premiums forever either. Term life insurance is exactly like renting. Buy the term for the period you think Marcello and Michaela will need it and hope you wasted your premiums."

"What do you mean?"

"You have fire insurance, don't you? You hope your premiums are wasted, right? For them to pay off would require a disaster: your house burning down."

"How's your time?"

"It's okay, I'm multitasking. I bid and now I'm dummy again. Where was I? With term insurance you hope that you don't die young and that you do waste your premiums. Just like rent."

"But I want some investments, along with my insurance now."

Sheena was standing nearby, listening to Jamie's half of the conversation. When he said investments he looked directly at her. She smiled and went back to the kitchen.

"What's stopping you?" Theo said, "Ever hear the phrase 'Buy term and invest the difference'?"

"Sure, whatever that means."

"It means buy term to deal with your insurance needs and only your insurance needs. If you want to invest, do so directly. You can invest the difference between the high premiums of whole life and the low premiums of term insurance directly, say in your retirement plan's mutual funds. You don't need the insurance company to do it for you and mark it up. Later, when you're much older, there may be some tax advantages to whole life, but for now I'd stick with term. Remember, your insurance needs change as your family and financial status change."

"Makes sense."

"Hang on, I have to play a hand. Stay on the line."

Jamie watched and refrained from interrupting him. Sheena had returned to give him a cup of tea. This morning naptime was bliss, Jamie thought guiltily, glancing with affection at the babies sleeping in their bassinets.

"What does Theo say?"

"He says for us right now, we should buy term and invest the difference."

"Told you," she said with that 'I'm always right' look she'd cultivated over the years.

"But when do we get to invest?"

Sheena shrugged and picked up the stacked laundry from the coffee table. Theo was back on the line.

"Can I ask one last question?" Jamie asked.

"Shoot."

"We'll buy term, but that means we have some money left to invest now?"

"Correct, although of course you could divert the difference to debt repayment. How's that going?"

"Just the student loans now, and the rate is pretty low. I think we'd be better off investing now. Victor has an amazing amount stashed away in his IRA."

"Individual Retirement Account? How long has he been in the States?"

"His whole life. After our parents emigrated from Italy, they settled in Malone. That's in Upper New York State. We were born there. I'd still be there, if I hadn't fallen for Sheena. So I'd like to do the Canadian equivalent of an IRA."

"That's the RRSP. Registered Retirement Savings Plan. Same idea. Two great things about it."

"It cuts my taxes. That's all I care about."

"Not true. You also care about Findependence. Tax-sheltered retirement accounts are the single best way to get there, once your debts are eliminated. In the long run, it's the fact that IRAs and RRSPs shelter your investment income from tax that makes them so powerful. Plenty of my clients have $1 million salted away in them."

"I could retire on that."

"Maybe. If you could get a 4% return from bonds, $1 million would give you $40,000 a year without touching your capital, though you'd have to pay tax on the withdrawals. But just deferring taxes all those years is worth something. It's certainly a priority over investing outside tax shelters."

"Why?"

"Taxable or non-registered accounts generate an annual tax liability every time they pay you a dividend or every time you sell something and have a capital gain. And if you have cash or bonds outside a tax-sheltered retirement plan, they're taxed at the highest rate. So high that once you factor in inflation it's hardly worth holding interest-bearing vehicles outside tax shelters. That's why I call them the leaky bucket."[5]

"Hold on a sec." If he could get the waking twin up before she started squalling, maybe Marcello would sleep a few minutes longer. Experience had taught Jamie to move fast. "Okay," he said, tucking the phone under his chin, "Michaela and I are back." He shifted his daughter on his shoulder and walked around the room. "I think of leaky buckets every time I change their diapers," Jamie quipped. "But we may need to invest that way eventually. Because of my employer pension, I don't have much room for my tax-sheltered retirement plan."

"Right," said Theo. "That's the Pension Adjustment at work. The more your employer puts into your pension, the less the government lets you shelter in your registered plan."

"But I can put $200 a month in it, just about what I'm saving by using term instead of permanent insurance."

"Good. Since you're a stock and plan to generate stock-like returns from your busi-

[5]The term originates with Canadian actuary Malcolm Hamilton

ness ventures, you want to balance it out by putting that $200 a month of retirement contributions into bonds. Later, when the mortgage is completely paid off, we can talk about starting a non-registered stock portfolio and something new called Tax-Free Savings Accounts."

"I heard about that. A TFSA is like Victor's Roth IRA, isn't it?"

"It is. And it's a great place to stash your emergency fund. I have to go. I'm declarer and have to play the hand."

"Bye for now."

As he hung up, Jamie glanced at the stirring Marcello, adjusted Michaela on his shoulder and gave Sheena a quick embrace with his free hand.

"Term it is," he said. "I'm going to invest the difference in bonds when I open my new retirement savings plan next week. We'll set up a pre-authorized chequing account and add to it automatically every month."

"That's wonderful, darling." Sheena pecked him on the cheek, took Michaela from him and handed him a brimming laundry basket.

"There are some other investing vehicles Theo thinks we should start to use," Jamie said, as he carried the laundry to the twins' bedroom, "but not until we pay down the mortgage. Time to put on our fatigues and become frugality guerrillas again."

Chapter 8

Could It Happen to Me?

[ROXY MUSIC, 1975]

Almost seven years had passed since Jamie and Sheena had appeared on Didi Quinlan's *Debt March*, when Jamie got a call from one of the TV show's producers. Didi was inviting them back, along with Theo, to talk about their financial progress.

Sheena initially tried to beg off. The twins were now three-and-a-half, she said, and she didn't want to leave them at home. Jamie wondered if the memories of her earlier humiliation weren't the main reason for her reluctance. After some cajoling, he extracted a promise from her mother to stay with the kids. Finally, Sheena agreed to go. So did Theo. It was a chance for a two-night mini vacation in Chicago.

The set hadn't changed much in the intervening years. The audience was seated in two banks of seats on the north and east side of the studio. There may have been just a hundred guests, but by judicious use of camera angles it was enough to present the illusion of a far bigger crowd. The real audience, Jamie had to remind himself, were the millions of viewers at home watching TV.

As before, Jamie sat closest to Didi's empty chair, with Sheena next to him and Theo farthest away.

The director gave the thumbs up and retreated from the raised platform. The cameras lit up and as the first chords of the *Debt March* theme sounded, Didi strode to her throne in the middle of the set.

Eye-catching in a masculine grey trouser suit and brilliant red silk shirt, Didi unleashed a 100-watt smile that would have been overpowering in real life but seemed somehow appropriate for television. Then she launched into her patter. Jamie had heard ratings had slipped but that Didi was determined to keep the show on the air. From the shows he'd caught in the past year, it seemed she had become more confrontational than ever, ready to humiliate a guest if it meant generating viewer interest and boosting ratings. Jamie agreed to return only after extracting a promise from the producer that Didi wouldn't push Sheena to tears again.

"Tonight, we'll take you back seven years," Didi began, and then cued the director to run the original clip of Sheena's teary failure to cut up her credit cards. Jamie felt this was a low blow, but Sheena held his hand and whispered, "It's alright."

After the clip ended they ran a bank commercial. Sheena giggled at the latest Spend'n Save pitch. Then Didi introduced her "old friends." *This despite the fact she'd never laid eyes on them since the last show.*

"Seven years ago, they were financial basket cases," Didi intoned. "And today? Let's ask them. Sheena?"

"We're in much better shape, because we became frugality guerrillas," Sheena said, addressing Didi rather than the camera. "We have no credit card debt left and there's just a year to run on my student loan."

"Marvellous," Didi said. As the camera panned across the audience, Didi whispered to Sheena to look at the camera rather than herself.

"I'm sure the $1,000 cheque we gave you last time helped. I think we can see our way to paying off the rest of your student loan this time around. How about a big round of applause for Jamie and Sheena?"

The audience obliged. Didi addressed Sheena again in her best motherly tone of voice.

"I understand there's been a major addition to your family?"

"Indeed, Michaela and Marcello are three years old and," Sheena smiled at Theo, "you'll be glad to hear we're making regular contributions to their education savings plans—every month, straight off the paycheque into an equity mutual fund."

"Fantastic," Didi said. She made the faintest imitation of clapping but it was enough to get the audience to follow suit.

"How about your mortgage?"

"We're whittling it down. After two years, we replaced the 35-year amortization schedule with a more traditional one amortized over 15 years. We can't always take advantage of the annual prepayment privileges, but we try and put at least something towards it."

Theo interjected. "The good news is almost half their mortgage payments are now going towards principal, so it should be downhill cycling from here."

"You did all this without any disagreements?"

Jamie squirmed, angry that Didi was trying to stir up trouble just to ignite controversy.

"None I can recall," Sheena said, turning to Jamie with a twinkle in her green eyes. "Would you call the bedroom furniture discussion a disagreement, honey?"

"Let me think," he said, "a 20% interest rate, raised voices, slammed doors, but that's ancient history."

"What about the pool?"

Didi's eyes lit up. "What pool?" The cameraman got the hint and framed Jamie and Sheena in a two-shot.

"Sheena wanted to spend $20,000 on a new swimming pool," Jamie said. "That was one of the few major arguments over spending that I've won in the last seven years."

"I thought it would be an investment in the twins' future," Sheena said. "But Theo said that, unlike education, we couldn't consider big consumption items as investments in human capital."

"No one ever said guerrilla frugality was easy," Didi said, spreading her hands. A murmur of agreement rippled through the audience.

"We didn't go entirely without. We bought a little splash pool instead, for $20. That's all you need for young children."

Theo smiled. "I showed them that $20,000 applied to reduce mortgage principal was like freeing up twice that amount in interest payments. That act alone probably sped up Jamie's Findependence Day by a year."

"How *is* that coming, Jamie?" Didi said this without looking at him. Instead, she focused first on the audience, then on the camera.

"On schedule. I've not moved it back or forward."

"July 4th, right?"

"Correct. The day I turn 50."

"How old are you today?"

"35. Still a long way to go."

"So other than the bedroom furniture and the pool, it's been smooth sailing?" She's like a bull terrier, Jamie thought.

"Just about."

"Just about?" Didi kept pushing.

"There *was* that little flap over the cottage," Sheena said.

"A cottage? My my."

"We were vacillating between getting a pool or a cottage. I argued a city home on the lake would be more expensive than non-lakefront properties, but cheaper than having a house in the suburbs as well as a lakefront cottage up north."

"There's some logic to that," Didi said.

"In the end, we did neither. Everything Theo said about the pool applied doubly to a cottage. Besides, Sheena and the kids can spend weeks every summer at her mother's cottage up north."

"You can't achieve financial freedom without giving up something," Sheena said. "Like the song says, you can't always get what you want."

"You've become quite an authority on dinosaur rock," Didi said, pausing for effect on the word dinosaur.

Jamie winced but took the bait for a free plug. "Yes, Didi," he said calmly. He told her about his online LP business. "VinylNation.com has become a vibrant online community for the boomer generation that grew up on vinyl recordings."

"You've become its most prominent spokesman, though you're younger than the average participant. I see your blog mentioned all the time on real media."

"Dinosaur media," Jamie couldn't resist. "Yes. I also write retro music columns for the traditional print press."

"Not bad for a gadget salesman. Do you still work at that high-tech retail outlet?"

"I've moved up to district manager at Tech Heaven," Jamie said, thinking Jharhid would be happy at the mention. "Under Theo's guidance, we've pumped most of my raises into debt repayment and contributions to our education and retirement plans. With taxes as high as they are, there's not much room for anything else."

"Tell me about it. You must be very proud of your clients, Theo."

"They're not officially clients. Although Jamie has a talent for worming free advice out of me. I consider them friends."

Didi played to the audience as she said, "Surely they must qualify as clients by now?"

"Not yet." The audience groaned on cue, as Didi continued to orchestrate their reactions.

Theo waited, then continued. "I'm happy with the debt side, but they've only just begun to accumulate significant investments."

"Cut them some slack, Theo."

"I could, Didi, but I'm doing the same thing you are. Trying to guide them with tough love. You do it on the debt side. I take it from there and push them to save and invest once the debts and mortgage are discharged."

"How do you feel about that, Jamie?"

"This way I don't have to pay his fees," Jamie said, "which speeds the arrival of Findependence Day."

"The fees can be partly tax-deductible," Theo protested.

"Don't worry. Next time we're on this show, we'll have your minimum $250,000 and then some."

"Shall we book you now?" Didi said, as the exit music started up, "That's all the time we have for this segment. Our next guests …"

■ ■ ■

For the next four years, Jamie and Sheena practised guerrilla frugality enough to reduce the outstanding mortgage principal to just $50,000. They kept the old cars on the road a little longer, seldom ate out and resisted the temptation to buy frivolous luxuries like a hot tub or an in-ground swimming pool. Slowly, they added to their tax-sheltered savings.

Rather than take expensive vacations abroad they vacationed at Clara's small cottage. That's where Michaela and Marcello, now in grade three, got to know their cousins. Sheena's brother Eamon had four children and her sister Fiona another three.

Unfortunately, that idyll ended suddenly on a glorious sunny day in July, when Sheena's mother passed away. Jamie couldn't believe how quickly Clara had spiralled downwards from a vibrant, fun-loving mother and grandmother to a sick old lady. The cancer that riddled her body had made her last weeks a nightmare of intensive care and morphine.

By the time of the funeral at All Saints, Jamie and Sheena were exhausted. Looking at Sheena's drawn face across the crowded reception in the church basement, Jamie was glad they'd left the twins with the neighbours for the day. Their seven cousins had raised the decibel level in the hall without the help of the minor Morellis.

Jamie sighed resignedly as he edged his way towards the food table, shaking hands with Clara's card buddies and Sheena's teaching friends. His stomach grumbled.

Even one of those tiny, tasteless tuna miniature sandwiches the church ladies served would taste great about now.

Reaching for a plate he forgot his hunger as he heard from the far side of the buffet raised voices over the clatter of the grandchildren.

"What do you mean there's no will?" Eamon's raised voice rose above the din. "I thought you were the executor."

"I thought you were," Fiona retorted, her face contorted with rage.

Jamie chanced it and joined them. "Is there a problem?"

"There's bloody well a problem," Eamon exploded. "It seems Clara died intestate. I can't believe that could happen in this day and age."

"Are you sure?" Jamie asked, glancing at both his in-laws. "Whenever I asked about it, Sheena said you were taking care of it, Eamon. I'm sure Clara told us you had her affairs in order."

And after all the lectures Theo gave us about estate planning.

Fiona continued to press the point. "We should go through the house with a fine-tooth comb," she said. "Maybe she misfiled it."

"I don't think so," Eamon replied. He set his plate down and ran his fingers through his thinning hair. "Before she went to the hospital I dropped in and asked her to show me all her financial documents. Everything was organized tidily in a filing cabinet. She said nothing about a will. I thought maybe it was with her lawyer or in her safety deposit box."

"It's not there," Fiona said. "I cleared that out two days ago."

"What was in it?"

Eamon turned to face her square on.

"A few savings bonds and some ounces of gold. I took my two pieces."

"That's a bloody nerve," Eamon said, wagging a finger at her. "How do we know there weren't 50 pieces, and you took the lot?"

"You can trust me, which is more than I can say for you," Fiona fired back. "Don't think I didn't notice the missing painting after you left her house that last time. That was her masterpiece. Everyone in the family wanted it."

Eamon took a step closer to her.

"Did she ever say who was supposed to get it?"

Fiona stepped back to keep her distance.

"Considering how much I was there during her illness, I'm sure she would have wanted me to have it," Fiona said, her tone defensive.

Jamie tried to get a word in. "What about bank accounts and investment accounts?"

"Not a problem," Eamon said. "They were held jointly with me so we could avoid probate fees."

"You control the money in the joint account?"

"Technically, yes."

"How do we know you aren't just transferring most of it to your personal bank account?" Fiona's accusatory tones cut like a blade through the hubbub.

Eamon looked uncomfortable.

"I knew about that arrangement," Fiona said, "which is why I assumed she'd appointed you executor. You'd better show us the statements right away and split it three ways."

"I'm not sure I'm legally obliged to do that," Eamon said defiantly.

"I can help you on that one," said Jamie, swallowing quickly. "There was a court ruling on that recently. I read about it. Unless you can legally prove Clara intended that money just for you, it has to be divided equally among all the siblings."

"Like I said, there are no legal documents." It seemed to Jamie that Eamon was struggling to remain composed.

"Then you're out of luck if your plan was to take it all," Fiona said, giving him a slow, appraising look. "And the more I'm hearing, the more I wouldn't put it past you."

"How much is in them?" Jamie asked.

"Not a lot. The bank account just had enough for day-to-day expenses. Her brokerage account is a bit of a laugh by our standards: a few hundreds shares of a bank stock and some underperforming mutual fund."

"Life insurance?"

"Enough to cover the burial."

"Still," Fiona said in a more conciliatory tone. "It would be nice to know how much money she had altogether. What did she live on?"

"Mostly, Dad's survivor pension and the usual government pensions," Eamon said. "All of which die with her."

Sheena now joined them. "I could hear you from across the room," she said with a slight frown. "What was the fuss about?"

"It seems Clara died without a will," Jamie said. "It's not clear who gets what."

"Not that there's lots of 'what' to get," Fiona added belligerently, with a glance at Eamon.

"What about the cottage?" Sheena said.

"That should go to us," Eamon said. "We're the only ones in the family that ever use it. I spent hours fixing the roof and the boathouse."

"Are you both crazy?" Sheena's red-haired temper flared up as she joined the fray. "Our kids have vacationed at the cottage every summer. Jamie has put the dock in and out for years with no help from either of you." She glared at her siblings, daring them to contradict her. "Don't think for one minute that either of you is getting the cottage. The only thing you can get is real." She was furious.

"You only spent the summers at the cottage," Fiona said, "because you were too cheap to take your kids on a real vacation." Fiona turned her glare on Eamon. "And your children are nearly grown," she said. "The only thing to do is sell the cottage along with the main house, then divide it amongst the three of us."

"Mom would have wanted to split her estate according to the grandchildren involved," Eamon said. "So we'd get four shares, Fiona three and Sheena two. Seems only fair the way Clara doted over those children."

Sheena gave him a scorching look. "That's totally unreasonable, Eamon, and you know it. You always were a greedy selfish bastard, but I would never have thought it could come to this. Mother had three children. Everything, and I mean everything, gets split three ways, and we all share. End of story."

"Easy, honey," Jamie interjected. "We can sort this out like civilized people. We need to consult an estate lawyer."

"The time to do that was before my mother died," Sheena hissed testily. "I can't believe you could allow this to happen." Her face was flushed with indignation.

"Me?" Jamie said. "She was your mother."

"You!" she fired back, green eyes blazing. "You were the great financial expert with all your plans for financial independence. All your consultations with the great Theo Konstantin. All your get-rich-quick schemes with Al Peters. What was I supposed to think?"

"You were supposed to think, period," Jamie retorted. "We did set up a will and power of attorney for you, me and the kids. I just assumed Clara had already been taken care of."

"And you know what assume stands for."

Jamie shrugged.

"*He's* the ass," Sheena pointed at Eamon, glaring at him. Eamon stared right back until Sheena averted her gaze. She turned to Fiona. Stuck for words, she blurted out, "Nice necklace, Sis. I haven't seen those pearls since mum wore them to Patrick's funeral."

"Pearls?" Eamon said indignantly. "Don't tell me you've nicked the pearl necklace she got from Dad for their 20th anniversary."

Eamon fingered the necklace to check more closely.

"Get your hands off me," Fiona said, her lips curling with disgust. As she stormed off, she gave a parting shot. "See you in court, bro."

"I've had enough. It's been a stressful day," Sheena said. "You've really disappointed me, Eamon. And on such a day as this."

"We'll sort it out. It's only money."

"If that were all it was, it wouldn't be so sad. I could live with your ridiculous proposal on how to split the money, but you went beyond the pale when you stole mum's favourite painting. Fiona's right. We're not going to let you get away with this kind of behaviour without consulting a lawyer."

"Which will consume still more money," Jamie said. "Wouldn't it be better just to come to a friendly meeting of the minds?"

"How much is that painting worth?" Sheena said. "To Fiona, maybe nothing. To me, it's worth $50,000. And what about the other jewellery and our childhood photographs and all the other things?"

"It's just stuff," Eamon said. "I'll give you that painting she did when she was in art school."

"The one that hung over her bed?"

"Yes, the light blue seascape."

"You mean you took that too?" Sheena exploded in renewed rage. "Who made you executor? Wait until Fiona hears about this. You're not the brother I remember, Eamon, not by a long shot."

Eamon just shrugged.

"Let's go." Jamie took her hand.

Sheena brushed him off, still glaring at Eamon. "Don't touch me."

■ ■ ■

Sheena knelt before her parents' tombstone. First Patrick, she thought, now Clara. The staff at All Saints Cemetery hadn't yet chiseled in the year of Clara's death.

Sheena removed the wilted chrysanthemums from around the gravesite and handed them to Jamie, tenderly replacing them with the fresh pink, yellow and white dahlias the children had picked from the garden that morning.

Jamie left Sheena to her thoughts and walked a circuit around the grounds. The skies were a dark grey, matching the greys and blacks of most of the tombstones. He inspected a few gravestones along the way, the sickly sweet odor of mixed floral arrangements assaulting his nostrils.

He tried in vain to imagine the lives of the departed. He paused at length in front of one tombstone that read, "As you are now, I once was. As I am now, you will one day be."

Earlier that August day, they'd resolved the inheritance squabble in court. Before Sheena's siblings followed up their legal threats with actions, wiser heads had prevailed. In the absence of a will and any friendly agreement between them, the judge ruled the proceeds from the two properties and the financial accounts would be split evenly three ways. Much of the money was earmarked for the nine grandchildren involved, placed in trust until they reached the age of majority. After the dust settled there was $52,000 left for Sheena.

When Jamie got back to Clara's gravesite, Sheena was ready to leave. They walked slowly through the cemetery grounds. "You have to plan ahead," Jamie said, thinking of Clara's rapid death. "Life's full of unexpected surprises."

"At least we've covered off our life insurance," Sheena said.

"Theo says we're nearing the age where we should insure against other possible events."

"Like?"

"Like disability insurance. At my age, I'm more likely to be disabled than to die."

"I have long-term and short-term disability in my group plan at work," Sheena said, somewhat smugly.

"How about critical illness insurance? It covers things like cancer, stroke and Alzheimer's." Jamie stopped walking and gestured toward the hundreds of tombstones around them. "If Clara had been covered, she'd have got a lump sum of $100,000 tax-free to help with bills not covered by government or employer health plans."

"I'd rather have had 20 more years with my mum than some death benefit." A gust of wind blew across them. Jamie hugged his wife.

"You might have got them. But what if she'd had a stroke and didn't die? She could have lived another 20 years. So could I, if I suffered a stroke. But I might not be able to work, and you'd find it expensive to take care of me. That's what the lump-sum benefit is for. Critical illness is a living benefit," he said, parroting what Theo had told him.

Sheena nodded.

"So are disability insurance and long-term care insurance. Living benefits," Jamie continued, "Life insurance is a death benefit. It pays your beneficiaries when you die. A living benefit pays when you're still alive but in bad shape. Or as Springsteen sang in Jungleland, if we have the misfortune to 'wind up wounded, not even dead'."

"How gruesome," Sheena said.

They paused in front of a granite mausoleum erected by one of the most prominent families at All Saints. It was lovingly maintained. At the entrance someone had recently placed a stunning arrangement of exotic cut flowers. Bird of paradise and lilies were the only ones Jamie could recognize. You could smell them from twenty paces.

"It's all part of life," Jamie continued. "It's too late for Clara, but it's not too late for us to get living benefits insurance. The longer we wait, the higher the premiums. Now we have some spare cash, we could initiate coverage and sleep better at night."

"Forget it," Sheena said. "Did you never read *The Wisdom of Insecurity?*[6] Life has so many possible paths and outcomes, it's impossible to insure against every possible disaster. Who said, 'Do not worry about tomorrow, for tomorrow will take care of itself'?"

"The Bible. But that was a different era."

Sheena dug in her heels: "Think of the cost of all those premiums. It would put a major dent in one of our full-time salaries to insure against everything."

"There's a happy medium. Life insurance is essential when families are young, but at some point living benefits may be more urgent. Or you can just self-insure."

Jamie shifted his gaze from the mausoleum to his wife. He felt anxious about her reaction to this conversation so soon after her mother's death.

"Self-insure?"

"Once you build a good investment portfolio, those funds can be used to take care of medical emergencies that aren't covered by the government or your employer's health plan."

"I can see if you invested all the money that otherwise would go to insurance premiums, you might be ahead of the game," Sheena said, "Especially if none of that bad stuff ever actually happened to you."

"It's a crap shoot," Jamie said. They started walking again along the main pathway of the cemetery. Except for a few squirrels, they were alone. "Again, a question of balance. In the end, no matter how much insurance you get, you can't fend off the grim reaper forever. For now, let's defer the decision on living benefits insurance."

[6]See appendix, A Peek at Theo's Library

"We still need to decide what to do with our portion of the inheritance." As they walked, the grey clouds turned black and a spattering of rain started to fall.

"That 50 grand applied to the rest of the mortgage would really speed up Findependence Day," Jamie said, quickening his pace, "Finally we'd be mortgage free."

"It couldn't make that much difference."

"It would. Two or three years, perhaps."

"You can retire ahead of schedule with your next wife, the one you'll remain childless with."

"Kids are great," Jamie said, "As my Dad used to say, 'I wouldn't trade one of my kids for a million dollars. And I wouldn't give a dime for another one'."

"I think we should stick most of the inheritance into the twins' education savings plans."

The raindrops were more numerous now.

"We save for days like this," he joked. "Anyway, we're already putting $5,000 a year into the twins' education plans, which should be enough."

Sheena, prescient as ever, pulled out her umbrella. Jamie crowded next to her. They headed toward the cemetery gates, now only a hundred yards away.

"We've been doing that since they were born," Sheena said, "so that's a good $35,000 between them we've already contributed."

"Plus they'll end up with $7,200 each in grants and investment growth," Jamie said, "And now they've also got all that inheritance money locked up in a trust."

"The money they got from mum is not earmarked for their education and they can't access it as minors. One day they could use it for a down payment on their first homes, start a business or travel the world."

"But we could also use your portion of the inheritance to speed up our financial plan. Can't we at least spend it the way we want to?"

"You mean the way *you* want to," Sheena countered. "If we're talking about spending, I wouldn't mind a real vacation."

"I didn't mean spend it. I meant investing it or paying down the mortgage." Jamie felt like a broken record, he'd repeated the line so often.

"That's so intangible. The day after we pay down the mortgage, the money's gone and our life is just the same."

The rain was pouring down now. They sprinted the rest of the way to the parking lot. Once inside the car, Sheena continued to make her case as she dried herself off. "Let's take a vacation," she said, "Replace the kitchen appliances and put the rest as a lump-sum contribution into the kids' education plans. It's an investment in their human capital."

"Aren't we overshooting?" Jamie asked, turning the key on the ignition, "How much does it cost to send a kid through university now?"

"If they live in residence, it could cost $60,000 to $80,000 each, over four years. More if they want to go to an Ivy League school or abroad. Then there's the possibility of grad school."

"They already have $25,000 each in their plans. Add to that a lump-sum of $20,000 each and they should be able to go to whatever schools they choose."

"So it's settled," Sheena said. "A vacation, appliances and the twins' education."

As Jamie pulled out of the driveway on to the main road, Sheena took one last look at the rain-spattered cemetery that was her mother's final resting place. Jamie was pretty sure those were tears mixed with raindrops on her cheeks.

Chapter 9

A Question of Balance

[THE MOODY BLUES, 1970]

After a decade of hard slogging, Al had built his part-time electronics importing business to the point where he felt he could go to the next level. He booked a booth at the annual Consumer Electronics Show, the Mecca for toys and gizmos. He persuaded Jamie to book a week's vacation from Tech Heaven to staff the booth for the entire show.

With its acres of commercial booths, where vendors mixed with suppliers, distributors, dealers and the general public, the sprawling Convention Centre resembled a country fair. The only difference was that, instead of rides and kewpie dolls, businesspeople peddled technological devices of all kinds.

Al had considerably toned down his usual flamboyant business attire. Today he wore a grey suit and a white dress shirt. But he continued to eschew a tie.

"Hey," he said, slapping Jamie on the back as he entered the booth. "Not bad."

He looked proudly around the booth. It was a standard entry-level unit located in an aisle far from the action. The main feature was a large plastic sign bearing the words Far East Electronica. In future years, he hoped to be closer to the big booths booked by the majors.

"I know we could use a little more sizzle, but at least you're enjoying some serious eye candy," he said. With a slight nod, he indicated some attractive young co-eds he'd hired to hand out brochures and smile at all who approached. "They're both majoring in business," Al said. "I promised they could spend three days in Vegas if they'd work the booth. Didn't cost me a cent. Paid for it with my points."

Al switched his attention to a pair of well-dressed businessmen who had been drawn to the booth by the shapely brunettes.

"Works every time," Al whispered. From their nametags, Al learned they were from a New York venture capital firm. He could hardly contain his excitement. He interrupted their conversation with the co-ed. "I'll take it from here, Jocelyn," he said.

The pretty undergrad shrugged her shoulders and walked away while Al introduced himself to the two men.

"Harry Berkowitz," the older one replied, extending his hand.

"James Stanton," said the younger, slickly dressed one. "Berkstan Capital."

"Which needs no introduction," Al said. "You guys are legends in this space."

Turning quickly to Jamie, he announced proudly, "Gentlemen, let me introduce you to my Director of Sales, James Morelli."

"But we never—" Jamie stammered, looking urgently into Al's eyes.

"Jamie is a rising star at one of the local Tech Heaven franchises," Al explained, "and something of a media celebrity."

Al directed their attention to a small device to the left of the booth. "This is just a prototype," he began. "One of many ground-breaking devices we're sourcing from a phenomenal low-cost manufacturer in Shanghai. We can undercut the majors by 50% and still make a killing. You know what that means to the bottom line."

He explained the major features and benefits of the gadget and fielded a staccato stream of questions on quality control, security of supply and timeliness of shipments.

Finally, Berkowitz, the senior partner, popped the key question. "How much do you need, and what do you think your company is worth?"

Al squirmed, realizing his answer could affect whether or not he retained control. Out of the corner of his eye, he noticed Stanton's attention straying repeatedly back to Jocelyn's ample cleavage. "Let's take valuation questions offline, guys," he said.

Al handed them each an engraved invitation. "We can find a quiet corner at our hospitality suite tonight after the show closes," he said. "Sushi and cocktails." Then, with a knowing look towards Stanton and a nod in the direction of the co-eds, he said, "They'll be there too."

The venture capital moguls stuffed their invitations into their pockets before moving on to the next booth. When they were out of earshot, Jamie said, "Think they'll come?"

"Hope so," Al said. "But they're not the only irons I have in the fire. You'd better be there in case. They seem to be big fans of Tech Heaven."

"Tech Heaven has nothing to do with Far East Electronica."

"Ah, but they don't know that."

As he patted his young friend on the back, Al's smile didn't seem to extend quite to his eyes. "These guys could be useful to us if we want to take this thing into the big time," he said. "The trick is to look bigger than you actually are."

Jamie didn't smile back. "This looking bigger than we are is getting time-consuming. My hours have gotten longer at Tech Heaven now they've given me more responsibility."

"Good. Hope you got a nice raise."

"It's like most big companies," Jamie shrugged. "Do the extra work first. The money comes later."

"Give yourself a raise, I always say. That's the beauty of moonlighting."

Al stepped three paces out of the booth to accost three young college boys with crew cuts. "In the market for state-of-the-art home theatre accessories?" he oozed. "We're the best. Here, take a brochure."

One boy accepted. "We're just here to scout the market for jobs," he said.

"We're hiring. Send me your resume." Al handed each of them a business card.

After they left, Jamie said, "You have people on payroll?"

"Not yet. At this stage, a network of freelance contractors still makes more sense. Why, would you like to come on full time as a real Director of Sales?"

Jamie shook his head. "Between Tech Heaven and Vinyl Nation, I don't have the time."

Al tried not to be too scathing as he lectured. "You'd be making a big mistake if you let a hobby web site stop you from getting in on the ground floor of a global import/export enterprise."

"It's a hobby now, but I have actual paying customers."

"I've seen your little chat room. Vinyl died two decades ago. You're flogging a dead horse."

"Don't be so sure. It's got great demographics. The people browsing the site are baby boomers with plenty of time and money. Most are financially independent or close to it."

"You with your Findependence Day. Stick with me and you won't have to work a day after 45."

Jamie looked dubious. "I'll be 40 next year."

"I know. Time to take a chance. How much does Jharhid pay you?"

"$65,000 base, but as district manager I also get a piece of the whole sales team's commissions. I should hit 80 grand this year, for the first time."

Al was deep in thought.

Jamie added: "What did you have in mind?"

"If I could raise some seed capital, I could use a guy like you."

"For what?"

"I need someone to close supplier deals in China and Vietnam and keep an eye on the sales pipeline."

"How often would I have to travel?"

"Once or twice a month. You'd love it. The women…." Then, catching himself, Al said, "The people are so warm and genuine."

"Salary?"

"With an override, I'd double your gross."

Jamie whistled softly. "What would my title be?"

"Like I said. Director of Sales."

Al detected the faintest trace of a frown in Jamie's face.

"I was thinking Director of Marketing."

"I'm Director of Marketing," Al said. "You could wear two hats and also be Director of Procurement."

"Sounds like a ton of work."

"I wouldn't be doubling your take-home pay for a walk in the park."

"Is that a job offer?"

"Not yet, but if I can get financing, would you consider it?"

"Depends. How about equity? I still don't have any skin in the game."

"If you want equity, it costs."

Jamie shifted his weight from one foot to the other.

"Money's still tight. Micki and Marco are growing fast. Seems every month we have to buy them new clothes. Doesn't sweat equity count for anything?"

Al looked Jamie straight in the eye: "Sure. I'll take care of you, don't worry about that. You should be good for at least 1,000 founder's shares. But if you want a major stake, we need more working capital. There are things we need to do that can't be done on the cheap with sweat equity."

Al glanced at the promo girls and winked at one of them. "Now her I'd love to share sweat equity with."

Al looked at his Rolex. "Well, think about it. Let's close shop and get to the hotel suite. You need to attend to a few details in case the big wigs arrive."

"Me?"

"You. You are the Director of Sales, aren't you?"

Jamie thought for a minute but didn't respond. He decided to treat it as a rhetorical question.

■ ■ ■

One sunny day late in September, Jamie dropped in on the Vinyl Cave, wishing Bernie had gotten around to air conditioning the place. Bernie's response to the unseasonable heat was to dress even more casually than usual: in shorts and sandals.

Jamie found Bernie at his usual spot by the counter. What little hair he had left was no longer grey but white.

"Bernie, can we update that financial plan you created for us? It's been more than ten years." Sheena had agreed that Jamie could spring for $500 for a progress report and revision to the plan. He waved a cheque for that amount.

It looked like business was slow. When the only other customer in the store left, Bernie locked the front door and flipped the "Out to lunch, back in an hour" sign so it faced the street.

They sat down in the small cluttered office at the back of the store. The thin screen monitor and notebook computer seemed totally at odds with the general squalor.

Bernie spread Jamie's financial files over a disorganized desk and pored over the bank and investment statements. Wiping the sweat from his forehead with his bandana, he flicked on a grimy old fan, careful to orient it so the airflow wouldn't disturb the papers.

"You're doing all the right things. One thing, though."

"Yes?"

"I notice you have a small investment account, invested mostly in speculative stocks. That isn't in your original plan."

"I get the odd tip from a friend in the import/export business."

"Doesn't look like they've panned out," Bernie said, as he peered through the reading portion of his bifocals and coughed into the bandana.

"I don't plan to quit my day job to become a day trader."

"Better not. My point was these stocks are held in a taxable account."

"Theo always said to hold bonds and cash in the tax-sheltered plans and stocks in taxable plans."

"That's a sound guideline though it's more complicated than that, especially with these U.S. shares you bought."

"How so?"

"The way interest is taxed you want your bonds and cash inside your retirement plan. But you also want foreign dividend-paying stocks there as well."

"I want the tax credits."

"The dividend tax credit applies only to Canadian dividends. You want to hold them in the leaky bucket, for sure. But foreign dividends are highly taxed, like interest or earned income. So put them inside your tax-sheltered plan."

"But these speculative stocks don't pay dividends."

"Right, these junior stocks you've gambled on are the furthest thing from blue chips and don't pay dividends. They can stay in your taxable plan. You may as well harvest some tax losses. Believe me, you have some losses here."

"But I made a big profit on the Internet stock."

"It just about equals the losses. I'd sell equal amounts of both before year-end to reduce your capital gains tax. But I was trying to make a couple of points."

"Yes?"

"One. Do you want to be making such speculative investments at your age?" Jamie nodded.

"And two, the same money can now be sheltered in a Tax-Free Savings Account."

"A TFSA? Theo mentioned that once. He said it's just like the Roth IRA that my brother, Victor, has in the States. He can save $2,000 a year in a Roth plan."

"They're both tax-prepaid savings plans, but there are some differences. The American version is less flexible and is focused on retirement. The Canadian version lets you shelter more in investments: $5,000 a year per person or $10,000 if you're a married couple."

"But it works like an IRA or RRSP?"

"Not quite. With either of those retirement savings plans you get a tax deduction up front that reduces your income tax the year you make the contribution. That's usually all that young people in a medium tax bracket care about."

"Right. Roth IRAs and TFSAs don't give you a tax deduction up front, which is why I've never bothered with one."

Bernie reached across to increase the speed of the fan. "Man, I need some water. How about you?"

Jamie nodded and Bernie went to fetch some. Looking around the cluttered office, Jamie chuckled. There were two jam-packed old metal filing cabinets, one grey, and one that would once have been beige when it was originally purchased. The file drawers didn't close properly and a few stray invoices were in danger of slipping out of the cabinets altogether. On top were a couple of plants that looked badly in need of watering.

"Here," Bernie said, handing him a glass of water. Jamie didn't stop to scrutinize the glass too closely.

"Now for the critical new element of your financial plan," Bernie said. "When you're older you're going to pay plenty of tax when you start withdrawing from your retirement savings. The beauty of Roth-like plans is that, when you take money out, it will be tax-free. That's because you already paid the tax when you first earned the money and paid income tax on it."

Bernie coughed again and took a slug of water. "The other thing about those withdrawals is they won't be counted as income when the government calculates old age pensions and certain other income-tested benefits. That's a plus."

"Maybe I should look into it, but where are we going to come up with another $10,000 a year?"

"Stop wasting your money on hot tips on individual stocks."

"But I hear about some great IPOs."

"You know what those initials stand for?"

"Sure, Initial Public Offering."

"No. It's Probably Overpriced." Bernie's laugh turned into a hacking cough.

Jamie grinned. "But with our pensions and our regular contributions to our registered plans, we have retirement savings covered off. It's not like I declared Findependence Day would arrive on my 40th birthday."

"Your plan is reasonable and you're still on track. But TFSAs are not just about retirement savings."

"No?" Jamie raised his eyebrows.

"No." Bernie cupped his hand to his mouth and whispered in a mock conspirational tone. "You might not want to tell Sheena this, but some financial planners think the S in TFSA could just as easily stand for Spending as Saving."

"Spending?" Jamie laughed. "We don't need help doing that."

"But you do. What happens when you want to save up for some big-ticket item?"

"Like a car?"

"Sure, a car. Say you want to save up $20,000 for a new middle-of-the-road family car."

"We've been thinking about that lately. Sheena's Corolla is held together with hope and a prayer."

"Have you put any money aside for a new one?"

"A couple of thousand is earmarked in one of our savings accounts."

"How much interest is that account paying?"

"Practically nothing."

"Even if it's nothing—and I'd consider 1% nothing—what happens at tax time?"

"They make us pay tax on the interest."

"So if you did manage to save $20,000 what would you get in interest?"

"1% of $20,000 is $200."

"You're in the top tax bracket?"

"Not quite, but I will be as soon as I make Regional manager."

"So you'll have to pay a third or more of that $200 as income tax next April, leaving you with about $140, right?"

"That's life," Jamie shrugged.

"Not if you put that money in a Tax-Free Savings Account. While you still wouldn't get a tax deduction on it, the interest would grow tax-free."

"Like the kids' education plans?" Jamie grabbed an LP from a stack on the desk and started fanning himself. "It is *hot* in here."

Bernie shrugged. "Same idea. But the TFSA is more flexible. You and Sheena could put in $5,000 each for a few years and add the accumulating interest and you'd soon be at your $20,000. Then you could withdraw it tax-free and buy your new car, lock, stock and barrel."

"Sheena would like that," Jamie agreed.

"It gets better. Unlike registered savings, when you withdraw that TFSA money, you don't lose the contribution room. As you accumulate more savings you can top up the plan based on the $5,000 a year per person limit. You can keep adding to it and withdrawing, depending on your goals. So it's great for consumption as well as saving."

"When you say saving, you mean just interest-bearing investments like GICs or money market funds?"

"No, you can invest in the same things as you'd hold in a retirement plan: foreign dividend-paying stocks, ETFs, mutual funds, the works."

"How about real estate?"

"You could also invest in Real Estate Investment Trusts, sure."

"Sheena's always after me to do what her father did and buy investment real estate."

"You're sitting in some here."

Bernie got up from the chair, switched off the fan and stepped onto the main floor.

"So I heard," said Jamie, walking beside him up the aisle to the front of the store.

On either side, old records overflowed from their bins. On the walls Bernie had stapled a continuous row of album covers, many of them depictions of psychedelic art from the '60s.

"I own the whole building. I live in an apartment over this shop. Plus I rent out the commercial space to the coffee shop and the dry cleaner next door. Each of them have tenants in the apartments above."

Jamie was impressed. "That must have set you back a lot."

"I bought when prices were much lower," Bernie said, "after real estate bottomed at the end of the last cycle. Remember, I spent almost three decades in the corporate trenches, just like you are now."

Jamie stopped walking and looked at his friend.

"That gives me an idea, Bernie. You and Theo are always talking about exit plans for your clients' businesses. Have you ever thought of selling the Vinyl Cave?"

"No," Bernie resumed walking back to the front of the store. "I don't believe in full retirement. I reached my Findependence Day, and this was my avocation. I like the social networking I get from my customers."

"They're a better-heeled crowd than people realize."

"Right. This store appeals to baby boomers getting nostalgic about their youth. Nothing like old records to remind them of past glories. I have virtually no competition. Isn't that what your web site is about?"

"You know about that?" Jamie tried not to look too surprised.

Bernie smiled. "A day doesn't go by when some customer doesn't mention it."

"I didn't realize. Maybe we could do a deal together. You want to get involved in the Internet?"

"Furthest thing from my mind. I'm happy the way things are." He flipped the "out to lunch sign" back to its former position. "I'll update your plan and e-mail it to you next week."

"Thanks for the update on tax-prepaid savings plans, Bernie. Wait till I tell Sheena the government just made it easier for her to spend money. There goes our guerrilla frugality program out the window."

■ ■ ■

For the next six months, Jamie redoubled his efforts at work. He drove his sales team harder than usual in a bid not only for higher commissions but to catch management's eye once a more senior position opened up.

It was just before annual bonus time when Jharhid asked Jamie to come to his office. He came armed with spreadsheets showing how his team had boosted sales quarter over quarter, despite having lost two salespeople to a competitor. Jamie had a knack for hiring and bringing on new talent, so he was confident Jharhid would finally come through with a promotion to Regional Management.

"It's been a good quarter," Jharhid said, scanning the Excel printout Jamie had handed him, "for both you and your team. I wish I could say the same for the rest of the region."

Jamie glanced at the photograph on Jharhid's immaculate desk. His young wife and boys looked shyly into the camera against the exotic background of an Indian village. It was the only personal touch on the desk.

"It's been tough since this latest economic downturn," Jamie sympathized, "You can hardly blame consumers for tightening their belts."

"No you can't. Everyone needs to cinch in right now."

Jamie didn't like the way this conversation seemed to be headed. "Maybe there's an opportunity for my team to push the other outlets in the district to higher levels of productivity." *If that's not a hint for a promotion, I don't know what is.*

Jharhid's face was pinched. He cleared his throat nervously.

"Jamie, that will not happen. We've been in global meetings for the past three weeks, looking for any other solution. But the only action we can take in this market is to downsize. Tech Heaven is eliminating 300 district level jobs across North America. Yours is one of them."

Jamie felt the blood drain from his face and thought for a minute he might faint. *This is what shock victims must feel like.*

Jharhid came around the desk and put his hand on the younger man's shoulder. Concern etched in the lines fanning out from his dark eyes.

"But, but …" Jamie stammered, "I've been with the company since college. I'm one of your best performers. You can't—"

"We can, and we must." Jharhid's voice was sad but firm. "Your severance and details are in the envelope. Take your time, read it over, and we'll need a signed copy back in a week or so. I think you'll see Tech Heaven is being quite generous and—"

"Wait," Jamie interrupted. "What about a job at Region or even back at the store level? There must be something."

"We've got good store-level people right now, Jamie. It wouldn't be fair to kick one of them out so you could stay. Besides, you wouldn't be happy with such a demotion."

Jharhid sat down again at his gleaming desk.

"You didn't say anything about Region," Jamie grasped at a straw. "I'm ready for a promotion. There must be a place there."

Jharhid cleared his throat and ran his fingers through his short, grey-flecked dark hair. Jamie had never seen him look so dishevelled.

"Jamie, we did review your name for the one possible Regional job opening. But a couple of managers were at the trade show and saw you working with Far East Electronica. One of them heard you introduced as their Director of Sales."

Jamie started to respond, but Jharhid raised his hand.

"I know. You told me years ago you were doing some writing for FEE. And the articles and blogging didn't hurt Tech Heaven either. But writing brochures is one thing. Publicly announcing you are Director of Sales for a major supplier, while holding a senior management position with Tech Heaven, indicates a serious lapse of judgement. Our executive decided—and I had to agree with them—that you weren't ready for the Regional promotion. I'm sorry, Jamie."

Jharhid looked him in the eye for a split second, then down at his desk, focusing on nothing in particular. Jamie's mind was elsewhere too. The scene at the Convention Centre ran through his memory like a bad video. He had to admit that, in retrospect, it looked bad.

"I understand, Jharhid. I'll get my things." Jamie picked up the termination papers and slowly got up from his chair. For the last time he walked out of Jharhid's office, gently closing the door behind him.

At that moment he wished he had never met Al Peters.

Chapter 10

When I'm 64

[THE BEATLES, 1964]

Jamie filled a box with a few personal possessions and left Tech Heaven less than half an hour after his meeting with Jharhid. *At least they didn't escort me from the premises.* He dumped the box in the trunk of his BMW, pulled out of the parking lot and headed—he didn't know why—toward the lake. That wasn't the way home, but there were hours to kill before Sheena would expect him.

He spied an available metered spot and parked the car, slamming the door. It was early April but the lake was calm, reflecting the grey sky. The only signs of life were a few seagulls and a dirty homeless person in tattered grey pants and a sweatshirt. The bum put out his hand hopefully. Jamie reached into his pocket and handed him a few coins.

What did I do that for? he wondered. *My own source of funds has just dried up.* He kept walking along the boulevard but slackened his pace. For once, he had nowhere to go and plenty of time to get there.

He replayed what had just happened. Jharhid of all people. I never saw it coming, he thought. It must have come down to Jharhid's hide or his own. Probably had no choice.

Sheena would have a fit. He pictured the shock on her face when he told her. She had no inkling there was trouble at work, but why should she? He'd been blindsided.

Thank God Sheena has a steady job, he thought. With the economy like this they'd be in serious trouble if they were both out of work. Jamie thought back to recent discussions about her teaching career. He couldn't recall her reporting any serious problems with the principal or even fellow teachers. *She's okay. She has seniority and a good union.*

What about the twins? They were eight now. Michaela and Marcello would be happy to see more of their dad, but would they understand? How would they react to an unemployed father hanging around home day after day?

Bernie's revised financial plan factored in two steady incomes. If worse came to worst, there would be several months of income from what was euphemistically called Employment Insurance. Despite the blow, Jamie smiled at his recollection of collecting pogy as a youth. It occurred to him E.I. was for people with an employee mentality: bonds. I'm a stock, he reminded himself. Time to start behaving like one.

Jamie realized he hadn't been that happy the last few years at Tech Heaven. He was grinding it out for the sake of the kids and his financial plan. Hanging in for the security of the micro-pension. He was glad he'd taken time to read that Alan Watts book Sheena had urged upon him over the years: *The Wisdom of Insecurity*.

Insecurity was now upon him and he could step into the void where all possibilities lay. What was good luck but the collision of preparation and opportunity? He'd been preparing for years, cutting debt and salting away capital for the moment when he could strike out on his own. Prepared, yes, but where was the opportunity?

Jamie had reached one of the downtown yacht clubs and cast his eye over the expanse of sea-going wealth that lay before him: cabin cruisers, sailboats, cigarette boats. He was willing to bet most of the owners were stocks, not bonds—entrepreneurs and businesspeople who worked hard and seized opportunity when it presented itself. But where are the customers' yachts? Jamie smiled as he thought of the classic investment book about stockbrokers.

He tried not to think about Findependence Day, which surely now was beyond his reach. He'd have to push back the day, but he was still young. He'd be back on his feet in a year, two at most.

Don't break into capital. Find new sources of income. Those thoughts hammered into his brain with every step.

Reluctantly, he conceded he still needed a job, the security of a salary and benefits. Vinyl Nation wasn't ready to break out and start generating the kind of income needed to sustain their comfortable middle-class lifestyle.

The Vinyl Cave? Not a big enough operation for Bernie to offer him a job. Good thing he didn't want to sell it.

His thoughts turned to Al and Far East Electronica. Damn it, he's why I'm in this mess, Jamie thought. He gave me the title. Maybe I should tell him I want the job. Why is it people offer jobs to people that don't need one? When you finally do, they sense the fear and back off as if you were a leper.

Forget it. The last thing Jamie was going to do was call Al about a job.

The details of the severance offer were burned in his memory. There would be one final paycheque plus two weeks pay for each of the almost 20 years he'd worked at Tech Heaven. That gave him almost a year to reorient and reassess his values. Perhaps Findependence Day was a pipe dream not even worth pursuing. What was so terrible about working after age 50? Most people did. Look at Theo and Bernie, Jamie thought. They're financially independent but continue to do exactly what they used to do.

But there was a difference. Theo and Bernie were working because they chose to.

Considering his still-fragile financial circumstances, he was in a different situation. He needed to keep working because he had to. I have no choice, he thought, unless I win the lottery or marry rich.

Neither was going to happen. With an increasing sense of desperation, he picked up the pace.

■ ■ ■

Still reeling from the shock of being laid off, Jamie tried to rekindle his fundamental spirit of optimism. Whenever he had encountered setbacks before, he'd responded with action.

But he'd never lost a job before. As he continued to walk along the lakeshore, the skies darkened and rumbled with the distant sound of thunder. As the first few drops of rain started to descend, he turned, breaking into a jog back to the car.

He was soaked by the time he reached it. *Now where?* Aimlessly, he drove a few miles, slowing to a crawl as the storm reached its fiercest. He could barely see through the windshield and noticed other cars had pulled over until the worst had passed.

He spied a Starbucks and pulled into a just-vacated spot. Over the years he and Sheena had been Froogers, his trips to this purveyor of premium coffee had grown less frequent. He hadn't forgotten Didi's televised rant about a daily coffee habit and other frivolous purchases.

But today, guerrilla frugality could wait. He wasn't yet ready to confront Sheena. The store was crowded as he plopped into the only remaining comfy chair. As the rain pounded against the window, Jamie replayed the scene with Jharhid. He felt a rising panic mount in his gut. *I've got to do something.*

He pulled out his cell phone. It might have to go, along with other luxuries-turned-necessities. That had been his stock-in-trade, convincing consumers they needed cell phone service, texting, Internet service, cable television, bigger screens and louder sounds. Gives a whole new meaning to the definition of need.

He scrolled through his phone list and saw Theo's number. What the hell. He dialled, and Theo picked up on the third ring.

"Odd time to call. What's up?"

"I just got fired."

"What? Last I heard from you, you were bucking for promotion."

Jamie told his friend about the scene in Jharhid's office, concluding anxiously, "Now what?"

"In the short term, you're in financial survival mode. Between severance, Sheena's income and Employment Insurance, you're okay for at least nine months. Don't panic."

Theo's voice sounded reassuring.

"I'm not." Yes I am, he thought.

"But don't kid yourself," Theo continued. "The way the economy is going, you could be out of work a year or more. You should hear the stories I get from clients. This brother-in-law is out of work for two years. That sister can't find anything but waitressing jobs. We're in a serious recession. Some might use a scarier word."

Jamie felt a knot in his stomach. If Theo was trying to make him feel better, it wasn't working.

"I'm pushing 40. I know it may take awhile."

"How's your emergency fund? Did you use Bernie's suggestion of keeping six months' worth of living expenses aside in liquid funds?"

"We've just got started so it's more like four months worth. It's earning high interest in a Tax Free Savings Account." So what was that lump he felt in his throat?

"Perfect," Theo said cheerfully. "If you need cash after your severance and employment insurance run out, you have it. When you're back on your feet, repay the account. Beats making withdrawals from your retirement plan and paying tax on it."

"It may come to that. We have more in our registered savings than in the emergency fund."

Jamie could feel his breathing returning to normal. Still, he gripped the cell phone tightly, as if he feared Theo would slip away from him when he needed him most.

"Bernie says some clients deliberately melt down their retirement plans." Jamie sipped his latte.

"They'd be in their late 50s or early 60s and have a lot more saved than you. I don't recommend it."

"Why not?"

Lightning flashed outside, bright enough to reflect off Jamie's coffee cup and make him avert his gaze.

"Those people have reached Findependence Day or are nearly there," Theo continued. "They may no longer be earning full-time employment income and are in a low tax bracket. They know when they reach their mid-60s they qualify for the usual government pensions. But if their registered savings get too large, once they start withdrawing from their plans they'll end up having benefits clawed back or taxed."

"I don't have that much."

"No. Those considering plan meltdowns often have more than $1 million in the plans. When they turn 71, they'll be obliged to withdraw 7% a year or more from them. Those withdrawals will be taxable, and they may be in higher tax brackets than they were after they first stopped working."

"A problem I'd like to have."

"Most older clients built up those plans before tax-free savings accounts were created," Theo said. "Depending on your tax bracket, you may want to save in a Tax Free Savings Account ahead of a registered retirement plan. Withdrawals from TFSAs aren't taxable, so you won't have to worry about the government clawing back means-tested benefits. Talk to Bernie about it, especially if you have a low income this year."

The panic attack that had seized Jamie's body had passed but was replaced by a dull feeling of apathy.

"I suppose age 50 was an unrealistic goal for my Findependence Day."

"It was aggressive. But remember, Findependence Day is not the same as Full Retirement. Age 50 is way too young for that. During First Retirement, you discover your true wealth is time."

Jamie smiled ruefully. "I have plenty of that now."

"This is a great opportunity to reflect on your transition to being[7]. You no longer have to be torn between the tradeoffs of time spent at work and time doing the other things life has to offer."

"But my whole life has been spent working."

"You didn't plan to sit in a rocking chair and watch daytime TV the moment you achieved Findependence?"

"Of course not. There's my music, my web site, my blogging—"

"There you go. Or you could go back to school and retrain for an entirely new career."

"Too old for that."

"Nonsense. You're not even 40 yet. Even at 50, a man can expect to live 26 more years. When she's 56, Sheena could also expect 26 more years. Plenty of time for both of you to reinvent yourselves."

"She'll be free and clear from teaching by 55."

"Government workers like teachers and politicians often retire at 55 with gold-plated inflation-indexed pensions. Corporate executives may have similar plans but enjoy the power and perks so much they usually keep working well past that age."

"Choose being the operative word. When do they stop?"

More lightning outside, followed seconds later with an ear-splitting crash of thunder. The whole coffee shop shook and briefly the background chatter ceased.

"Some stop at 60, the earliest they can take reduced Canada Pension Plan benefits. The normal age is 65. But now we're talking about the Second Retirement, when you really slow down and figure out what defines you apart from work."

"Victor says he has to wait till 67 to collect Social Security."

"You could wait that long if you chose to. Each year you delay taking CPP, the payments would be 6% better."

"So you're telling me I should wait till I'm 70 for Findependence Day?" The thought of liberation slipping into old age threatened to turn Jamie's apathy into depression.

"If you did, your benefits would be 30% more than starting at 65 but only if your goal is to maximize income in Full Retirement. The fact you set age 50 as your Findependence Day suggests to me not the Second or Full Retirement but a wish to recreate yourself. The question you have to answer is how and what? As an artist? An entrepreneur? You've been given the gift to find out which."

"All of the above, I guess. The sooner I start, the better." Dad never lived long enough to enjoy his retirement savings, Jamie thought.

"So there are no government pensions to be had as early as 50," Jamie said. "But what if I started withdrawing from my registered plans then?"

There was a silence at the end of the line. Jamie was sure that, if he could see Theo's face now, he would be frowning. "In theory that's possible," Theo said finally.

[7]Courtesy EES Financial

"It's a little known fact you can start withdrawing from your registered plan that early. It may not make sense tax-wise, because you want to keep the tax shelter maximized as long as possible. Some clients do want to accelerate withdrawals well ahead of schedule. Nobody should retire at 50. But Findependence is another matter."

Another loud clap of thunder but Jamie was feeling emboldened. He needed Theo onside now so he could pick himself up and get on with his goals.

"Right," Jamie said. "Financial freedom is welcome at any age. The earlier the better. I don't want to wait till I'm too old to enjoy my leisure. That was the mistake my dad made. Seems to me the only way to jump-start the process is to start a business, build it up and sell when the time is right."

"Can't argue with that. That's precisely what many of my best clients did."

"They were lucky to have you advising them. Come on, Theo, this has gone on long enough. I need you now. Let's do the paperwork and make it official."

Jamie glanced outside. It had stopped raining and a ray of sunshine was struggling to break through the cloud cover. Several customers who had come in solely to escape the downpour were leaving.

"Not yet, Jamie, but it won't be long. Bernie is helping you, isn't he?"

"Sure, but he's not you. Can you tell me if I need to move my Findependence Day back a few years?"

"Not my decision to make," Theo said firmly. "Only you and Sheena can decide that, with Bernie's guidance."

"At least tell me if I should look for a new job or try to start a business." Jamie tried to keep the panic out of his voice.

"Listen to your heart. Talk it over with Sheena. I have to go now. Ariana is giving me the sign."

Jamie closed up his cell phone, gazing at the last of the rain dribbling down the windows. He didn't move for a long time.

■ ■ ■

Jamie had hoped to bounce back quickly enough that he'd be earning double pay— collecting severance on top of a new salary—which would have brought him more quickly to his Findependence Day. But by mid-summer he was still out of work.

The daily news of the struggling North American economy remained unremittingly depressing. To stay on schedule to reach Findependence Day by 50, he needed to find work before the end of summer. But with each rejection from potential employers, his confidence sagged further.

The twins were now in grade three, and the expense of clothing, feeding and amusing them did not let up. Job interviews dried up, and it was harder to maintain his enthusiasm when checking the classifieds and online job sites.

When he did go online, he often ended up playing online poker or chatting with his growing number of buddies at Vinyl Nation. He was still mailing out a few albums, but this was a slim reed on which to build his hopes.

One evening after the twins had gone to bed, Sheena grabbed a chair in the den and drew it close to him. "We need to talk."

Jamie flipped back to the job site, drawing her attention to the monitor. "I'm registered here. Tons of jobs. I'm being selective."

"That's BS and you know it. After a few months lying fallow, I'd hoped you'd get serious about finding a job. How much longer am I supposed to be the sole bread-winner in this household?"

"I'm selling records around the world."

That reminded him. He flipped through his latest vinyl acquisitions and put on an old Led Zeppelin album. The worse he felt, the more he was comforted by such despairing tunes as *Dazed and Confused.*

"You can't even afford to buy them from Bernie."

"He knows I'll get back on my feet. But it's looking like this drought could last quite a bit longer."

"How much longer?"

"How should I know? Weeks. Months."

"One thing's for sure. It won't be years. If you don't start standing on your own feet before the fall, there are going to be big changes around here."

Jamie looked down. The balance of power had shifted between them. The longer he was out of work, the more anxious Sheena became. It was the reverse of when she was on maternity leave, when he was the main breadwinner and in control. He smiled as he recalled his father's version of the golden rule: He who makes the gold makes the rules. Problem was it was a she who was making the gold now.

"Sheena, I don't know what you're suggesting, but it would be easier to stay afloat if we didn't have this huge home. I know we've paid off most of the mortgage but it's the other expenses that are killing us. Property taxes are out of this world, heat-ing and hydro bills keep rising, and it costs plenty to keep up appearances in this neighbourhood. By downsizing, we'd have money in the bank."

Theo had made these points whenever he called to raise Jamie's sagging spirits. But Sheena wasn't buying it.

"The twins are supposed to live in a hovel? You were all for plenty of space when you thought Vinyl Nation would be a going concern."

"If we'd moved to a more affordable house in an older district in the first place, we'd be in a far better position today," Jamie said. "We could sell this place and downsize to something cosier. Our re-sale value is high here. We could wipe out the mortgage altogether, buy a smaller place and maybe have a hundred thousand dollars to spare. I had Bernie run the numbers. It would improve our monthly cash flow."

He looked down, absentmindedly flipping over the jacket to the Zeppelin album.

"Is that your financial plan?" Sheena said, running her hand through her hair. "Keep doing nothing and suck all the equity out of our home as if it were some kind of ATM?"

He looked her in the eye and said in a steady voice, "I'm not talking about bor-rowing on the home. We've built up plenty of equity here. By moving to a cheaper home, we'd no longer have any monthly mortgage payments at all. We'd have money in the bank, money to invest and live on, and lower expenses to boot."

Sheena gave him one of her patented Irish scathing looks.

"Have you considered the twins?" she said. "They turn nine next January. All their friends are here."

"They'll make new ones. How often are you in touch with the friends you had when you were their age?"

Jamie pulled out his cell phone, preferring to glance vacantly at its display than look Sheena in the face.

"I'm more concerned about our friends today who live just a few blocks away. Jamie, we've laid down roots in this community. There's everyone at church, the people we've met through the twins at daycare. You can't just uproot the whole family because you can't be bothered finding a job."

"I'm looking every day." He grabbed the remote and raised the volume a tad.

Her tone was becoming icier by the minute. "You haven't e-mailed a resume in three weeks. I'm tired of this."

"Sheena, that's not fair. You know the firing was not justified." Jamie stood up, pushing a stack of albums out of the way with his toe.

"Then you should have sued them for wrongful dismissal." Sheena raised her voice, frustration etched in her face.

"How could I do that to Jharhid?" Jamie had considered suing and had even consulted a lawyer, but Sheena didn't need to know that.

"How could he do that to you?" Her voice shook with restrained fury. "When it came to choosing between his career and yours, you found out where his priorities lay."

"It's too late to go down that road anyway. I signed the severance agreement and cashed their cheques. Better to spend the energy finding work or building a business."

"I don't see much building happening here." She looked around the den. Jamie was suddenly conscious of the old newspapers and half-finished books strewn on the couch and coffee table. Piles of records were stacked in front of the stereo, some of them out of their jackets.

"These things take time," he tried to stay positive. "I'm thinking there may be more potential with the blog and chat room than on the mail order side of it."

She tidied the newspapers and put one of the records back in its jacket. Then, sarcastically: "And you would make it a business how?"

"Selling more banner ads or maybe charge a small annual membership fee. Since I added my Classic Rock blog, traffic is way up. I try to update it every day."

"Don't these retiring baby boomers have anything better to do than read online rants about half-century-old records?"

Jamie got up and flipped the record to side two, adjusting the balance between the speakers.

"It's not just online. Some newspapers and magazines have picked up the column."

"How much do they pay?"

Jamie turned back to face her. "Nothing. I'm writing the blog for the fun of it."

"That was fine when you were earning a regular income. Now you're not. Call those editors and demand payment. They have freelance budgets. Even token payments would help out around here. Send them invoices. Time to start acting like a pro."

"Can't hurt to ask," Jamie agreed. "I could probably make enough to live on if we could just cut our overhead."

"Jamie," she said acidly, "Get this through your head. We're not moving."

■ ■ ■

As July slipped into August, the atmosphere at 38 Verdant Crescent cooled appreciably. Jamie no longer pretended to look for work, played online poker well into the night, slept till noon and often neglected to shave. Sheena ceased to cajole him and regarded Jamie as an unkempt border she couldn't evict.

The only time he had any sparkle was when he returned from an excursion to the Vinyl Cave with some new musical gem Bernie had sourced. He'd listen to it to death for a few days, usually at high volume, then dash off a blog post about it. If he felt inspired, he would turn the post into a column for one of the papers. The cheques were small, but sufficient to stave off the execution warrant that Sheena implied was just around the corner.

A year had passed since Jamie had worked Al's booth at the trade show. Apart from a few more copy-writing assignments, he'd heard nothing more about a full-time job with Far East Electronica. So when Al called one day out of the blue and invited him to a meeting, Jamie was receptive.

Far East Electronica was one of many small businesses in an industrial park in the suburbs. There were thousands of similar complexes in the country. This one was nothing special. As for the FEE headquarters mentioned on the door, Jamie had seen bigger sporting goods stores. Still, he had to admit the sign over the window was impressive.

Jamie cooled his heels in reception for a good ten minutes before the attractive young receptionist said, "Mr. Peters will see you now, Sir." She ushered him into a large well-appointed office. Al sat behind his desk. It was over-sized, imposing yet immaculate. Jamie noticed flecks of grey hair at the temples, but otherwise Al hadn't changed much since they'd last seen each other at the electronics convention almost a year ago. He was finishing a telephone conversation. "Tell him we're not paying a dime over the normal rate," Al said into the phone. "I don't care if it's held up at the border, just expedite it."

He hung up and swivelled around in his "I'm in charge here" chair. "Jamie," he said. "How nice you could take the time to visit our roaring enterprise."

"Things seem to be going well."

"We manage to make payroll," Al said. "It's like feeding a family. Guess you know all about that."

"Lately, Sheena's been the one bringing home the bacon."

Al paused and fixed Jamie with what seemed to be a sympathetic look.

"I knew you and Tech Heaven had a parting of the ways. Pity. But that was some time ago?"

"About four months."

Al looked up at the ceiling but didn't seem to focus on anything in particular. When his gaze returned to Jamie, he said, "I'm sure you've had more than your share of job offers. You're well regarded in the industry."

Silence. After a moment Al broke it with, "Did they give you a coffee out there? Water? Juice?"

"Water would be fine, thanks."

Al punched a button on his phone. "Joyce, could you bring us a water and a coke?" Then, to Jamie, "You're consulting?"

"You could say that. Blogging. Some writing for pay."

"I've seen your Classic Rock column in the music rags. But look, you wouldn't be here if you didn't think there was some work I could throw your way."

"I'm not looking for part-time contracts. I would however consider a full-time position."

"Full-time you say?" Al paused, swivelled his chair to face the window and steepled his fingers.

"We talked about that a year ago."

"Things are different today. You know how bad the economy is."

"I'm aware of that."

A knock on the door, and one of Al's attractive young assistants brought in a tray with the beverages. "Thanks, Joyce, you're a doll," Al said. She just smiled. Al didn't take his eyes off her till she'd shut the door.

"I had to let go of some clerical staff a few weeks ago. The great American consumer is sitting on his wallet."

"All the more reason you need an ace Director of Marketing," Jamie said. "You know advertising and marketing are needed most when times are tough. The best marketing directors pay for themselves many times over."

"It's an important role, but I can do that one myself," Al said. "Now a director of sales, on the other hand, that would be a useful function."

Al looked him in the eye. Jamie met his gaze for a second before looking down. He took the cap off his water and gulped back a refreshing slug.

"You have an opening for a Director of Sales?" *That was the title that cost me my career at Tech Heaven.*

"Depends how you define the job. There's always room for a good salesperson. A self-directed one, if you get my drift."

"How much does it pay?" Jamie looked Al in the eye and promised himself he'd win this round of the staring contest.

"Less than you hope. I don't take a salary myself."

"You don't?" Jamie was surprised.

"Not much of one." Finally, Al looked away, glancing at his watch. "The money boys control the board, now that they've put in a second round of financing."

Jamie's eyes narrowed. "The angel investors?"

Al smiled. "Yeah, the slave-driving bastards. They want to see profits before big salaries. They hate overhead with a passion."

"So no base salary?"

"None, I'm afraid. Naturally we can do a draw against commissions and put through lots of expenses." Al smiled and popped open his can of cola.

"I'm a good salesman. Depending on your program we might make it work, as long as you remember I have a family to feed."

"That's what lines of credit are for, my boy," Al said, repeating his life's credo. "Although I know you're committed to this Findependence Day thingy. How's the campaign coming anyway? To me, it's all about how big a line of credit you qualify for."

"It's on hold. And we have a line of credit I'm not allowed to touch." Getting the conversation back on track, Jamie asked, "What territory do you want me to cover?"

"Eastern seaboard. I know you don't like to travel too far." He took a sip of Coke and then used his hand to wipe a few stray drops off his lips.

"I'd be OK with that. Sheena never used to like my business trips, but these days she'd probably be happy if you gave me South America. Or Antarctica."

Jamie smiled. Al didn't.

"So you accept the eastern seaboard?"

"Tempting. What's the bonus structure? Profit sharing and equity ownership? I'd think 10% would be appropriate given my involvement getting FEE off the ground."

"Equity is never free. Ten per cent is not on, but I might be able to see my way to finding 5%, provided you inject a little capital."

"How much?"

"$50,000."

"Al, if I had that much to spare, I wouldn't be here talking to you."

"Borrow it. The interest is tax deductible."

"I'll talk to Sheena. If it were up to her alone, I could start yesterday but…." Jamie's voice drifted off, and he stared vacantly at a corner of Al's desk.

"Jamie?"

"Sorry. I was thinking back to the show last fall. The one where you said you'd take care of me."

Al scrutinized his face. He wasn't smiling.

"Yes?"

"I'm sure you mentioned something about a thousand founder shares."

Al leaned his chin against his jaw, covering most of his mouth. "There've been a few changes since then. I've cut in quite a few new investors. If you want to be a player in FEE…"

"Fee?"

"FEE would be the ticker symbol on the New York Stock Exchange. Anyone who wants to buy Far East Electronica can just specify FEE."

Jamie raised his eyebrows.

"NYSE? I'm impressed. And it's easy to remember."

"It might have to be a more junior exchange to start with. But FEE will be the ticker."

Al waved a brochure from one of the stock exchanges. "But that's only one route we're considering," he continued. "The angels want to see a track record of a few more years before implementing their exit strategy. If the market stays down, we could stay private and sell to one of the big boys."

Jamie nodded, feeling out of his depth when it came to high finance.

"So you'll talk to Sheena about the 50 grand?" Al said.

"OK. But how much of the company would that buy?" As an afterthought, Jamie added, "She'll want to know about the founder shares, too."

Al fixed him with a stare. "Get the 50 grand, and perhaps we'll throw them in," he said, avoiding an answer to the far more important first question.

Al crumpled the brochure into a ball and tossed it into the wastepaper basket.

Chapter 11

Taxman

[GEORGE HARRISON, 1966]

Sheena was delighted when Jamie told her he might be working again soon. Any work was better than moping around the house all day, even if it was with Al Peters.

Jamie had his doubts. He was looking forward to talking with Theo. When he called his friend, Theo invited Jamie and Sheena for dinner a few days later at their downtown townhouse. They would talk then.

The front yard of the Konstantins' townhouse was minuscule, but Ariana's green thumb was clearly in evidence. Freshly painted black shutters framed the picture window and purple geraniums flourished in the flowerbox below. When they arrived, Ariana led them into the backyard, where Theo was scraping the barbeque. There were still a few weeks of summer left. Jamie could hear the faint rumble of a streetcar along a nearby street.

"Right on time," Theo said, brushing off some BBQ debris from the apron he'd tied neatly around his waist.

The backyard was not much larger than the front, but the Konstantin children had long since left the nest, and the couple had adjusted their living space almost immediately. A partially enclosed brick patio extended almost to the edge of the property, beyond which a row of tall cedars enclosed the yard from the neighbours.

"What can I get you to drink this fine summer day?" Theo said. "Corona with a slice of lime?"

"You read my mind," Jamie said.

Sheena and Ariana were already talking about the kids. Theo caught Jamie's eye and the two went into the house, stepping directly from the terrace into a cozy den.

"Nice townhouse," Jamie said.

The den reminded him of a public library. Books were neatly arranged in categories: business, investing, philosophy, religion, history.[8] Jamie picked up an investing book at random, flipped it open and noted many passages were neatly highlighted in yellow. "You've read all these?" Jamie said.

"At least once," Theo smiled. "That's the great thing about achieving financial independence. Plenty of time to read."

---

[8] See also appendix, A Peek at Theo's Library

They proceeded to the kitchen to get the beer.

"Tell me about this job offer," Theo said, slicing up a lime while Jamie flipped the caps off the bottles.

Jamie provided the details on the way back outside, including the fact he could purchase a small minority position in Far East Electronica for $50,000. Theo looked dubious but said nothing.

As they rejoined their wives outside, the two men clinked their Corona bottles. Theo told Ariana Jamie's long spell of unemployment might be coming to an end.

"That's wonderful," Ariana cried, giving Jamie a hug. "That must be a relief for you too, Sheena!"

Sheena laughed. "You don't know the half of it."

The foursome settled back into comfortable chairs in front of a small wrought-iron table.

Theo looked serious. "It's a bit complicated. Is the job contingent on making that investment?"

"No," Jamie said. "Al talks about going public but even as a private company, it would be nice to get in near the ground floor."

"Do you have that much spare cash?"

"We have enough equity in the house to get a hefty boost in our line of credit," Jamie said. "Since it's an investment loan, we could deduct the interest charges from our taxes."

"You trust Al that much?" Sheena said. "Tell him about the founder shares."

Jamie shrugged and sipped his beer.

"You know how I feel about leverage," Theo said. "Conservative leverage may work for certain investors, but this doesn't qualify."

"But I know this company well, because I work there," Jamie said. "Don't they say you should invest in what you know? Like the kids who invested in Disney or McDonalds?"

"It's still an individual stock and a speculative one at that," Theo said, frowning like a stern schoolmaster. "Didn't Bernie warn you against such investments? If it were me, I'd pass. If Al gives you a job regardless, that's all you want."

Jamie tried not to show his disappointment but kept pushing. "What would your idea of conservative leverage be?"

"Two things." Theo stood up to put some steaks on the BBQ. "One, the loan would be only a small percentage of your total financial assets. On that score, you probably qualify now. I take it you're getting close to the $250,000?"

"Nearly."

"Second, it would have to be invested in a broadly diversified portfolio of blue-chip stocks, perhaps a well-managed Canadian equity mutual fund or an exchange-traded fund like the Diamonds."

"Diamonds?" Sheena seemed suddenly interested. She flashed her ring at Ariana, who did the same with her own diamond necklace. They exchanged knowing looks.

"It's an ETF that provides exposure to the 30 large stocks that make up the Dow Jones Industrial Average," Theo said. "Blue chips like General Electric, Pfizer and Microsoft."

Jamie mulled this over before adding in a subdued tone, "I can see that's not quite the same as putting it all on Far East Electronica."

"Not by a long shot. And if, as I suspect, a $50,000 investment would account for 25% of your financial assets, that's way too much for a single speculative investment. Too many of your eggs in one basket."

"But I work there so I can watch that egg very carefully."

Theo pursed his lips. "No. It's never a good idea to have that much exposure to a firm that is also your employer—particularly if you don't have control. Look what happened to the Enron employees who invested their pension money in Enron stock."

"That's different."

"The plaintive cry of the poor investor—'This time it's different.' How about some wine?"

Approving looks all 'round.

"I'll get it, hon," Ariana volunteered. "I can see you're on a roll. Though I hate to miss the best part of this little chat."

Theo seemed both grateful and annoyed. "I was just getting to a review of our strategy. Sheena, what would you say our general approach is?"

"Multiple streams of income," Sheena replied. "Didn't you lend Jamie a book with a similar name?"[9]

"Correct. I wondered what had happened to that book. Everything I've ever told you revolves around that concept."

"That and Didi's guerrilla frugality," Jamie said.

"Precisely," Theo sniffed. "Ideally, the base is two sources of employment income, like an airplane with two engines. If one conks out, the other can take you to safety."

"It's a good thing this little engine kept on chugging," Sheena raised her eyebrows as she glanced at her husband, "after his employment engine conked out."

"These days it's tough to raise a family on a single income," Theo said. "In the early days of paying down a mortgage, it helps if you can earmark that second income for annual prepayments."

"It would be impossible to pay it down on just one income," Sheena said. "Little wonder so many one-income couples take decades to pay for their home."

"But as we've seen, with two decent incomes it should be possible to pay down the mortgage and maximize contributions to your retirement plans. That's certainly what Ariana and I did early in our marriage."

"Before the kids, naturally," Ariana interjected with a grin. "Now I really am getting the wine."

[9] See appendix, A Peek at Theo's Library

While Ariana left, Jamie and Sheena stood up and watched Theo finish barbequing the steaks.

"Sheena, you'll have your teacher pension, and I assume, Jamie, that you rolled your Tech Heaven Defined Contribution pension into a Locked-in Retirement Account?"

"Yes, I can't touch it until I'm in my mid-50s at the earliest."

"What other income streams do you have in place?"

"There's the Tax Free Savings Account, and the twins will eventually draw income from their education savings plans."

"So what's missing at this stage?"

"It's all covered off."

Theo fussed with the steaks a little more. "Medium rare okay with everyone?" Jamie and Sheena nodded and Theo continued. "What about rental income?"

That brought Sheena back to life, "I told you we should buy an investment property. That's how my granddad made his fortune."

"Rental income or distributions from REITs provide a solid base of regular income," Theo said, flipping the steaks. "There's favourable tax treatment, and you can always sell the property if you have to and realize some capital gains."

"You're always going on about non-registered investment portfolios," Jamie said.

"Ah yes," Theo said. "The leaky bucket."

"Leaky bucket?" Sheena repeated.

They walked back to the patio table and sat down.

"Taxes. Sometimes because of limited room for tax-sheltered retirement savings, it's necessary to invest extra funds outside a tax shelter. The leaky bucket is one of the first things you should liquidate when you need extra funds. A taxable portfolio creates tax liability on all interest and dividend income, and also capital gains if they're realized."

"Realized?" Sheena asked.

"Say you have a $10 stock that quintuples, like Jamie hopes Far East Electronica will do one day."

"I have a thousand shares, or so Al led me to believe."

Sheena looked skeptical but held her tongue.

"Great!" Theo continued. "Say the stock rises to $50. If Jamie sells to take a profit, that $40 capital gain would be taxable. But as long he just keeps the shares, there's no tax due until he crystallizes or realizes the profits by selling.

"The point is," he continued, "a taxable portfolio generates three types of tax liability, which is why I call it a leaky bucket. That's why some experts say it's futile and don't even bother with taxable investments. They may have a point, too, now Canada has the equivalent of the American Roth IRA."

"Right," Jamie said, "Who has the cash for the leaky bucket after you've filled all the non-leaky buckets? Counting the kids' education plans, I can count at least three of them now."

Theo nodded in agreement but said, "You'd be surprised. People with very high incomes need to put their excess capital someplace after filling all those non-leaky buckets. They're happy to invest in taxable portfolios, but they know all their gains or income will be taxed. Nothing much they can do about dividend or interest income, but by refraining from taking profits by selling their stocks, they can defer capital gains taxes indefinitely, even in the leaky bucket."

"What about other tax shelters?" Jamie asked.

"Not a lot of them left."

Ariana returned with the wine. She handed Theo the opener.

"I have a friend who uses charitable giving tax shelters," Sheena said. "Buy low, donate high."

Theo shook his head while simultaneously opening the wine bottle. There was a loud pop. "I'd avoid those. The government is auditing everyone who got one. If it sounds too good to be true, it probably is."

"How about flow-through limited partnerships?"

"They're legit. Some of my doctor and dentist clients try some of them, but often what they gain in taxes they lose in the underlying investment."

The cloud that had obscured the sun drifted away. Theo put on his sunglasses. "The government encourages flow-throughs," he said, "because it wants people to invest in enterprises that explore for minerals and energy. Those are normally riskier than blue chip stocks, so they dangle a tax-sweetener to encourage investors."

"But it's also possible to make money on those investments on top of the tax savings," Jamie said.

"That can happen, and when it does, it's a double win. With any tax shelter, especially new ones, you have to realize there's more than the usual amount of risk and make sure you consult your accountant or tax lawyer before proceeding." Theo peered over the top of his sunglasses and added sternly, "If you don't understand it, pass."

"We're not in that snack bracket anyway," Jamie smiled.

"Even those who are sometimes end up wasting too much time and money trying to avoid taxes. You've heard the expression 'Don't let the tax tail wave the investment dog'?"

Jamie grinned. "Sounds painful."

"It sure can be. Venture capital funds are another example. Some governments provide tax credits on them. Perfectly legal, but investors often end up losing more in the risky underlying investments than they gain from the 30% tax credit or whatever is offered in the region you live. The joy of immediate tax relief is soon eclipsed by the long-term pain of negative investment returns."

"Doesn't sound smart."

"Sometimes the best thing to do is just suck it up and pay the taxes, then find the best investment you can, purely on its investment merits."

"If we had any extra cash to invest, it would go in the leaky bucket."

Theo poured the wine into everyone's glass. "Nice Australian Cabernet," he said approvingly, glancing at Ariana.

"Yes, Canadian dividend-paying stocks go nicely in the leaky bucket, because the dividend tax credit lowers tax payable," Theo said. "But I'd maximize the $10,000 a year you two can put in your TFSAs first. Remember, they can hold stocks as well as interest-bearing investments. Have I forgotten any other sources of income?"

"How about royalty income?" Sheena said. "You remember my launch party last year when I finally published my 'tween' novel?"

"How could I forget?" Theo smiled. "That was quite a blast."

"After ten years of work, I should hope so," Sheena said. "But the good news is that every once in a while out of the blue a royalty cheque shows up in the mailbox. It's like found money."

Theo nodded. "Right, and that may continue over your whole lifetime, as song-writers and artists are delighted to discover."

"Like that woman who composed the hockey theme song," Jamie said. "Da da da da da *dahhhhh*."

Theo laughed while Sheena put her hands to her ears.

"Good example. Wish I'd come up with that little jingle myself. So Jamie, now we've put all this into perspective, have we helped you with your decision about Al's job offer?"

"I'm disappointed you don't want me to borrow to invest in FEE stock. I may regret it, but I guess I'll pass."

"What about the job?" Sheena asked, anxiously.

"Oh I'll take the job," Jamie said without hesitation. "The commission structure is good, and I'm itching to get back into sales. Once Al realizes I'm indispensable, he'll up the ante."

Sheena smiled.

■ ■ ■

"Have a seat," Al said to Jamie one morning, waving at one of two chairs in front of his imposing desk.

Five years had passed since Jamie had joined Far East Electronica, and the depressed economy and financial markets had slowly recovered. After Jamie's second year at the company, Al had added a salary component and bonus to his commission arrangement and sweetened the benefits package.

Al was glad he'd increased Jamie's responsibilities, adding new sales territories and a team of sales reps to his workload. Too bad the kid hadn't taken a little risk to put some skin in the game, he thought, as Jamie sat down.

Still, Jamie had come through on every other front. Revenues exceeded expec-tations every year, although the angel investors were still pushing for a stronger bottom line. Price/earnings multiples had fallen during the tough times, and it took more profit to justify the same valuation.

"Seems to be going well with your team."

"You see the monthly reports," Jamie said. "Central's ahead of target, West Coast's on track, North's breaking all records. In the South we could use a new man ... or woman. All my travel and long hours are paying off."

"Guess you know why I called you in."

Jamie shifted his posture, raising his hands quizzically.

"I wanted to update you on the latest from our investors."

Jamie's face relaxed.

The angel investors had come on board after Berkstan walked away. Since then, Al told Jamie the angels' fluffy little wings had turned into horns and sharp instruments of torture. In fact, Al had felt constrained by Berkstan's constant oversight and board control, and he was secretly delighted to replace them with the surprisingly easy-to-schmooze angel investors. They'd put up only $1 million rather than the $5 million minimum Berkstan insisted on, but Al was able to keep control of the company, while creating the illusion to outsiders like Jamie and other small investors that he was at the mercy of the angels. The downside was it took a few more years to develop the business.

"They've been very patient, you must admit."

"What do they have in mind?"

Looking across the shining mahogany desk, Al thought Jamie looked every bit his 45 years, despite the classic white dress shirt and blue suit that he wore. Or maybe because of it.

"The usual. They're talking to some big integrated manufacturers in Japan and Taiwan. Always happy to pick up a strategically positioned supplier."

"Would that affect us?"

"Whatever they decide, it will affect us. But from the hints they've dropped, I'm guessing they're finally thinking IPO."

"They want to go public? That's been your goal from the get go."

Al paused and retracted his gold Cross pen. "I never expected it to take this long either," he said. "But finally the time appears right."

"Which exchange?"

"Probably Nasdaq or London."

"Either way, you'd be set."

"It could have been a nice payday for you too."

Jamie's face darkened. He knew the shares he might have bought five years ago with a $50,000 investment would be worth ten times as much today, maybe more, when the company went public. There was an awkward pause before he stammered, "If I'd sprung for that $50,000 when you offered it to me, this exit opportunity would have been my ticket to freedom."

Al tried to tone down his smile. "You snooze, you lose. But don't beat yourself up. You're earning a good salary. You've pocketed nice bonuses and commissions."

"Sure. Enough that we now have a financial advisor who accepts only mass affluent clients."

Al tried to look impressed. "High net worth?"

"One step below."

"Anyone I'd know?"

"Doubt it. Older guy named Theo Konstantin."

Al closed his eyes, trying to conjure up a face to go with the name.

"Doesn't ring a bell. The point is, the money guys are taking a more hands-on approach. They're sending in consultants, making recommendations that are, in effect, orders."

"What's my part in this?"

"A big one."

Al got up from his desk and stepped in front of a mounted wall map. The countries where Far East Electronica currently operated were colored green, while countries it hoped to penetrate were yellow. Everything else was a dull brown.

Pointing with his gold pen, Al touched North America.

"They want higher revenues in existing territories, of course, but they're pushing us to establish brand new turf in markets we've not yet touched."

"Like?" Jamie remained seated.

"Eastern Europe, Central America, maybe even establish a beachhead in Africa." With a sharp whack of his pen, he pointed to each territory.

Jamie nodded. "Ambitious."

"The idea isn't so much to build up revenues in those places. They're gussying it up for sale. If they build sales projections in several new markets into the prospectus, it will look good to investors."

"Makes sense."

"From their perspective. While I may appear to be the boss here," he gestured to indicate his office and desk, "we know who's really calling the shots." He wanted to emphasize to Jamie how little control he had over the company. The more Jamie believed that, the better.

"That's life in the big city."

"Indeed." Al walked back to the desk but stood behind it, leaned forward and planted his hands on the desktop, an effective way to intimidate his underlings, he'd found. "Unfortunately, it's you who'll have to experience life in a few of those big cities."

Jamie shifted his position in his chair. Al waited for his response.

"You want me to travel where?"

"Mexico City, Budapest, perhaps Johannesburg." Al took a step back to the map.

"I know where they are," Jamie said curtly. "Look, Al. The twins are in their early teens. I'm already away almost two weeks every month. This will make it even tougher to be a good Dad."

Al sat down. "They won't care. I presume daddy no longer enjoys 'can do no wrong' status?"

"It's more that I'd miss them."

"Is it a problem for Sheena?"

"Not like it used to be, but she usually doesn't like the single mum routine when I'm travelling. I'm not sure if going out on the road more would drive us apart or...."

Al tried his best to look understanding. He'd known full well that Jamie would balk at the increased time away from home. "Or absence makes the heart grow fonder?"

"Maybe so. I presume I don't get much say in this?"

"Not a lot."

Then Jamie's spirits seemed suddenly to brighten, the opposite reaction to what Al had expected. He noticed the faintest hint of a smile on Jamie's face as Jamie gazed out the window for a few moments.

"It would be an opportunity for me, I suppose," Jamie said at last.

"How so?" Al asked, baffled. Something weird going on here, he thought.

"I take it there'd be some flexibility in how I manage my time abroad?"

"The usual rules. Get the business done. What happens in Vegas stays in Vegas. Or Rome."

"I wasn't talking about that. You'd have no objections if I did a few things for Vinyl Nation?"

"Your hobby site? What kind of things?"

"Source a few records if I can find any shops still selling vinyl in those locations. But mostly, I'd want to build the network."

"The network?" Al wasn't sure where Jamie was going with this.

"The community of people who've congregated at the web site now runs into the hundreds of thousands, from across the world."

Al tried not to look surprised.

"They include participants from most of the markets you've mentioned. I could set up appointments with them, leverage their contacts and set up local chapters. It would help FEE as well. Kill two birds with one stone."

Al cocked his head, placing his thumb under his chin and index finger below his nose. "I had no idea," he said. "Are you making money from this?"

"Not a lot. Theo would call it just one of many income streams. More like an income rivulet really."

"How do you make money at it?"

"Still a bit from the vinyl mail order operation," Jamie said. "And I charge a $10-a-year subscription for those who want the premium service."

"There are two levels?"

"Yes. Lots of the content is free, including my blog. By the way, I'd also want to blog from all those locations."

"What do you charge for?" The kid's got more going on than I realized, Al thought.

"Access to the business-to-business listings, the home-swapping and vacation-swapping micro-site and finally, of course, the dating site."

"Wife swapping?" Al laughed at his own joke.

"That might happen on occasion, " Jamie laughed.

"It's a more viable enterprise than I'd imagined," Al said. "Perhaps I should have taken you more seriously." *There could be a real business opportunity here for me after all.*

"It all happened by chance," Jamie said. "Serendipity. And some of those early writing assignments you gave me helped open some doors."

"Glad to hear it. But the vinyl thing did seem out of left field."

"I know. Dinosaur rock. But it turns out those retiring baby boomers have enormous affection for the music of their youth."

"Something we all had in common."

Jamie was animated now. "It's not just the underlying music. After all, the music itself can be ported to CD or iPods. The real appeal is the actual physical packaging that came with their first experience of the music. The big art covers, the liner notes, the sound of a needle falling into the groove."

"I bought my share as a teenager," Al said. "Wish I'd hung on to some of them. All that money wasted when I replaced them with CDs."

"What did you do with the originals?"

"Threw 'em out on the curb. Yard sales. Whatever. Never thought about it at the time. Kind of miss them now. I had all of Deep Purple, Black Sabbath, Grateful Dead." He pounded a fist into his open hand. "Damn! I thought they were worthless."

"So did most people your age. I was too young to buy them when they were in all the stores. What an exciting time to grow up."

"You remember the *Sticky Fingers* jacket from the Stones?"

"With the do-up zipper?" Jamie laughed. "I bought it from Bernie's. Did you ever try to unzip it?"

"Of course. You just don't get that on CD!"

"Or how about the posters and photos that came in the White Album and other Beatles albums?" Jamie said. "Or the Uriah Heep *Look at Yourself* cover with a mirror that showed your reflection? Or the holographic cover of *His Satanic Majesties Request*?"

"Who knew?"

"If I told you how much those albums are going for, you'd have a coronary."

"Hundreds, I guess?"

"In mint condition, way more," Jamie said. "So, once the web site attracted a critical mass of baby boomers to talk about music and the good old days, the next thing I knew, advertisers were lining up to run banner ads to sell them cut-rate travel, mutual funds, you name it."

"So I take it you have no objection to any of the travel requests our friends in New York may impose on us?"

"I still worry about not being there for my kids," Jamie said, "But if I have to go, I'll make the best of it."

■ ■ ■

With six direct reports and the new title of Director of Global Sales at Far East Electronica, Jamie was feeling good about himself again. He could hold his head high when he returned home to 38 Verdant Crescent after long business trips like the one he'd just taken to Eastern Europe.

Jamie dropped his bag in the hall and entered the cozy den, but Sheena didn't bother to look up from her laptop. Though Jamie didn't object to his gruelling travel schedule, Sheena hadn't been at all pleased, and it looked as if she hadn't changed her mind. It wasn't so much that she missed him, Jamie reflected. But when he was gone, Sheena had to take on all the chauffeuring duties. Between soccer, parties and sleepovers, it seemed, the twins had friends in every part of town.

With the extra income he earned, Sheena had transformed their house into a true haven. Gradually, using cash they'd allocated to the purpose over time, she'd replaced the draperies and installed hardwood and ceramics warmed by thick oriental area carpets. She'd upgraded the furniture and added some prints and original paintings to the walls. It was no longer a house but a home.

As Jamie walked into the den, Sheena remained engrossed in writing what he presumed was another uplifting novel for the pre-teen market. Wearing jeans and a T-shirt and no makeup, with her shiny red hair pulled back in a ponytail, Jamie thought she looked as beautiful as the day he'd married her.

"Where are the twins?" he said. He was looking forward to a relaxing evening with the family.

"Just dropped them off at a birthday party down the road," Sheena said without looking up from her keyboard.

"Too bad," Jamie said. "I could use a hug."

"They'll be home in a few hours."

"I'm starving. Started dinner yet? I can rustle up a salad."

"Order Chinese."

"Okaaaaaaaay … How's it coming?"

"How's what coming?"

"Your book. The sequel?"

"For all you know, it's a prequel. You barely managed the time to read the series' opener."

"Travel. Got to take care of business." Jamie grabbed the appropriate junk food brochure from the basket, picked up the phone and ordered.

"It'll be here in 40 minutes," he said when he hung up.

"That's nice," Sheena said, still typing away.

"How's school?"

"Same as ever."

"Twins?"

"Still alive."

Jamie fetched his laptop and parked himself on the couch next to Sheena. "Mind if I catch up on the site? Seeing how you're engrossed in your own project."

"Why would I mind?"

"Seems you're happier when I'm in another part of the house or the continent. Maybe we need a vacation, spend some quality time with the twins."

"Take them to the zoo."

"Together I mean, the four of us."

"You travel so much. I figure when you're home you want to stay here."

Silence. Jamie signed on to Vinyl Nation and whistled when he saw the number of registered users online. Bowing to the community's wishes, he'd split the forums into two streams: Pop Culture and Money. Several cyber-identities self-policed the forums. The acknowledged regulars in Pop Culture called themselves Princess, Pop Tart and Shankshaft. In the Money stream, Old Hand, Advisor Guy and Greek Tycoon had developed loyal followings. Some, like Nimrod, were considered authorities in both forums.

"Over a thousand at one time! Sheena, do you realize what a huge milestone this is?"

"Congratulations." She had yet to look up from her own work.

"What's eating you?" Jamie said, setting his own computer aside.

Sheena finished typing a sentence, then finally shut the laptop.

"What's eating me? I never see you. Whenever the twins want to be ferried around the city, I'm the only taxi they can flag down. I never have time for my book. I do all the laundry, the shopping and the cooking, not to mention my full-time job. Then you breeze in from your little junkets and expect me to drop everything, get supper on the table, supply your every need."

"I'd hardly say every need. When was the last time—"

"The point is," she interrupted, "I've had it with all this travel. I've had it with you. I'm tired of being alone and making all the decisions. You need to be around more to help. And you never let me buy anything. Any money you do get, you want to invest."

"Sheena, everything's going to plan. Just five more years if we keep pushing."

The tense silence between them deepened. Now it was Jamie's turn to shift his focus to his laptop. Sheena just stared at the floor. A few minutes passed. Jamie exchanged online greetings with a few Vinylheads. All he could hear was the clattering of his keyboard and the faint sound of the kitchen clock.

Finally, Sheena broke the silence.

"Jamie, the only family time we get is our annual spring break in the sun."

Jamie remembered the year after Sheena's mum died, when the family sold Clara's cottage and Sheena and Jamie took their first trek to the sun with two energetic seven-year olds. Since then, planning for an all-inclusive week every spring had become part of their family tradition. Now the kids were in their teens, Jamie wondered how many more spring vacations they'd take.

"You know the twins read all your blogs posted on your travels? They want to connect with you."

Glad that the chill seemed to be lifting, Jamie said, "Do they see my video reports on You Tube? Sometimes they're picked up by cable TV."

"They're thrilled when that happens."

"Heard from Theo or Ariana lately?" Jamie asked.

"No. We saw more of them before he officially became our financial advisor."

"I'm seeing him next week for a review. Want to come along?"

"I'll pass. Finance is your thing. I want to break the back of this sucker." She motioned towards her laptop. "Ask him why there still doesn't seem to be much extra cash. It seems every month we're just breaking even."

"That's because we don't want our chequing account to hold much cash. It pays almost no interest, so it only makes sense to keep enough for regular payments."

"But you have so much money coming out for regular payments, we need thousands in there. There's the monthly pre-authorized chequing account for the kids' college funds, both our retirement savings plans, our tax-free savings accounts—"

"Which is why I'm working all the time, honey. I love closing a sale and investing the commission in the market."

"And now I see there's yet another debit swooshing out funds automatically," she said, ignoring his interruption, "What's that?"

"The final step of the plan. Theo said it was time to start building up our non-registered investments."

"The leaky bucket?"

"Right, the taxable plan," Jamie grinned. "But you'll also notice all those dividend payments coming in now. Several hundred dollars a month."

"But we never get to spend them. You just reinvest them."

"Theo had me set up Dividend Reinvestment Plans—DRIPs—at the discount brokerage. The dividends are pumped back into buying more shares in the same stocks. It's a brilliant way to build wealth, and with no extra commissions. We can do the same with some of our mutual funds and ETFs."

"Great. Until we have to pay tax on it in April."

"Sure, there's a bit of tax, but receiving regular investment income is a nice problem to have. It's not a big deal if you accrue for it. That's where the short-term cash in the TFSAs comes in handy."

"You must be pleased with yourself."

"I like the feeling of having our finances under control. I like the idea we can see some light at the end of the tunnel. Think about how you'll feel when you reach your own Findependence Day."

"I think about it, but for me, 55 is still ten years away."

"I know, but think of the freedom you'll enjoy then. Instead of writing your books on nights and weekends, you'll be able to do it during the working day. Then your nights and weekends will be free for other recreations."

Sheena nodded. She looked almost wistful.

"You'll no longer have to endure the stress of simultaneously raising a family, working for a living, keeping the house going and then trying to steal a few hours for creative projects," Jamie continued.

"Sounds appealing."

"We can travel when we want, volunteer, visit the grandkids—"

"If we have any. You know Michaela has a boyfriend now? Of course, she just calls him 'a friend who's a boy'."

"No kidding. Takes after her mum."

"I guess. But Jamie, couldn't you get a job where you don't need to travel so much? Or talk to Al about your schedule?"

"Five more years, babe. Five years, that's all we've got," he sang a snippet from a David Bowie tune.

"I can see how your dream of financial freedom is worth achieving. I'm just not convinced we'll share it together."

Jamie blinked. "What are you saying?"

"Does your financial plan include my future pension and government benefits?"

"Sure, eventually, including the income when you start withdrawing from your registered investments. The same goes for mine. It's just a big pot we share."

Sheena paused and looked him straight in the eye.

"What if we don't go the distance?"

Jamie scratched his nose. "Well, then everything's cut in half. Probably we'll both have to keep working a lot longer."

"No more Findependence Day."

"Not by age 50, you're right. I just assumed you're in it for the duration. Till death do us part and all that."

Sheena grinned. "Sometimes I could kill you."

"And I you," Jamie said, "but we can always find a way through. If you've read *Stumbling on Happiness*[10], you'll know the teen years are actually the unhappiest for most parents. When the twins graduate and get married and we're out of the workforce, our happiness will soar, statistically speaking."

"They quantify that?"

"The author did: Daniel Gilbert."

Sheena had almost been smiling, but her smile faded to a frown. "My point is," she said, "I'm not so sure you should count me in your financial plan."

"What are you saying, Sheena? You want out?"

"I'm not saying that. But face it, we're having problems."

"We've systematically added every stream of income we could afford. What else is there?"

"Real estate. For the last ten years, I've told you a zillion times I want to buy land or some investment real estate. I need something tangible, not just electronic digits in a computer bank somewhere."

"We've got this house, and financial assets are just as real."

"Not to me they're not. What if Theo siphoned off all those investments?"

"They're not even housed with him. They're with a discount broker."

She pursed her lips.

[10]See appendix, A Peek at Theo's Library

"Well, what if some cyber-criminal broke in and transferred it all out?"

"Unlikely, since most online brokerages guarantee the full amount in the account against such an event. But we'd also have a little business income from Vinyl Nation and ultimately our workplace pensions and government pensions."

"I want the reality of bricks and mortar, and maybe some precious metals or gold coins," Sheena said, "They're the only things that are real and tangible. You know what they say about land."

"What do they say?"

"They're not making any more of it."

Chapter 12

Crash, Boom, Bang

[ROXETTE, 1999]

"Hey kids," Jamie said to the twins over a rare family supper one evening. "You busy this weekend?" Over that summer, Jamie was trying to spend what little time he had away from the office with the family.

Michaela gave him one of her scathing teenaged looks. "Duh, Dad. What did you have in mind?" Marcello kept munching on a hamburger.

"Uncle Theo invited us to the yacht club for an afternoon of sailing. There aren't many more summer weekends left."

"Didn't know he had a boat," Marcello said between bites.

"He doesn't any more. One of his clients offered it to him for the day. Thought you guys could put those sailing lessons you've been taking to good use."

"One sec, Dad." Michaela whipped out her cell phone and texted a friend. After a few moments, she got a reply. "Okay, Dad, I'm good. I've cleared the decks for some bonding time on the boat."

"How about you, Marco?"

"Sure, whatever."

■ ■ ■

That Saturday morning, they drove to the Lakefront Yacht Club. Jamie punched in the code Theo had given him and passed through the gate to the boats. He heard someone yell and saw Theo waving about 100 yards away.

As they often did, the twins took off in a footrace, with Michaela winning the race to get to the boat first. By the time Jamie got there at his leisurely pace, Marcello had unmoored the boat and was getting some basic instructions from Theo.

The day was dazzlingly bright, with only a few wisps of cloud on the horizon. From the clip they were moving at, Jamie guessed there would be wind aplenty for a good sail. As he stepped aboard, he noticed the boat's name: *Free At Last*.

Once they'd cleared the harbour, Theo handed Marco a cap with a sun visor. "Here, try this." Marcello accepted it gratefully. Theo let him take over the rudder, and they chatted about his imminent return to high school.

Michaela was on the prow, sunning herself in her bikini.

Once Theo was confident in Marcello's sailing skills, he caught Jamie's eye and cocked his head towards the cabin. He pulled two bottles of carbonated water from the tiny refrigerator and offered Jamie one.

"How do you like the *Free at Last*?" he asked with a grin.

"The perfect name," laughed Jamie. "If only it were true for me."

"You're getting there. Believe me." Theo pulled a printout from his vest pocket and laid it out on the small cabin table. It was a spreadsheet of the Morellis' entire financial situation. As Theo scrutinized it, he removed his sunglasses. "Good, good," he muttered. "Let me double check. There are no liabilities on your household balance sheet whatsoever?"

"No, nothing. We'd hoped to pay off the rest of the mortgage after Sheena's mum died but it didn't work out that way."

"That would have been the painless route."

"Don't I know it?" Jamie grinned, "And we couldn't pay it down after I was fired. Once I was back on my feet again with Far East Electronica, it took just three more years of pre-paying $15,000. So we've been mortgage free for two years now."

"How sweet it is. Student loans?"

"Ancient history."

"Credit cards?"

Jamie made a face. "We use just two cards for convenience now. We might put $1,500 or $2,000 on them in any given month, but we pay them off in full each month to avoid interest charges. If Didi taught us anything—"

"Good. There was a time you needed her tough love. Guerrilla frugality!"

"She's doing the same shtick with a new generation. Always the same thing." Jamie shook his head. "Up to their ears in debt, spending like crazy, not a clue. Froogers like you and me are an endangered species."

Theo glanced again at the printout. "If you are indeed debt-free that means your net worth just about equals your financial assets plus your house. With other clients, I usually have to subtract a big number for liabilities."

"It was a great feeling when we got that mortgage monkey off our back." Jamie looked through the cabin window. Blue sea as far as the eye could see, offset by a darkening sky. "The kind of freedom you must feel every time you go sailing."

"Nothing like it, although after a while Ariana and I found it too much of a burden maintaining our own boat. We're happy to be non-owning members of the yacht club." Theo smiled and took a swig of water. "In a way, owning a boat or burning a mortgage is a bit anticlimactic. You may feel that way about reaching financial independence."

"How do you mean?"

"You focus for five or ten years paying down the mortgage, but the moment you get there, what happens?"

Jamie closed his eyes for a second and thought about it. "It feels good for a few days, and there's less money coming out of the bank account every month. Then I guess you take it for granted and forget about it. Human nature."

"But there are always plenty of other expenses," Theo said. "You start to wonder how you ever managed to make the mortgage payments in the first place."

"That's right. In our case, we just invested more. Instead of $2,000 swishing out every month on the mortgage, $1,500 went into investments. We did allocate an extra $500 a month to our spending account," he added with a grin.

Through the window, he'd caught Michaela's eye. She waved at him from the prow of the boat before returning her attention to the teen magazine she'd brought with her.

"Teenagers are costlier than small children, we're finding."

Theo grinned. "I'm surprised you've found as much for investments as you have. Your net worth appears to be in the low seven figures, including your home."

"Yeah, but a million isn't like it used to be," Jamie said, half proud, half apologetically, "It was a long hard slog and we're still not where we need to be. I'm spending a lot of time watching the market."

"That can be stressful," Theo said sympathetically, "You own a lot of individual stocks."

"U.S. and Canadian dividend payers, mostly. Bond substitutes, Bernie used to call them."

"Hmm. Where I come from a stock is a stock and a bond is a bond. What did he mean?"

"During the last bear market, he found some financially strong blue chip companies whose stocks reached such good valuations that their dividend yields were higher than the interest paid by bonds. Over time, they would grow their dividends so they'd beat inflation."

"If you're doing that, I'd keep them to no more than 20% of your fixed-income allocation. Even with high yields, the value of the stock itself could fall. To be safe, I'd count those as part of your stock allocation rather than fixed income."

Theo continued to scrutinize a printout of Jamie's investments. For a moment, the only sound was the crackling of the short-wave radio, which warned the waters were getting choppy.

Finally, Theo was satisfied he understood Jamie's investments. "Outside North America, you still seem to be buying high-fee global mutual funds, although you've picked some good ones. If you go that route, I'd stick with the deep-value go-anywhere funds."

"I'm not unhappy with my actively managed mutual funds. I guess the high fees don't help in a roaring bull market but when the market is down I feel better with a value guy at the helm."

"If you're comfortable, no reason to mess with it. The active managers turn over their portfolios more, which generates tax, so keep those funds inside your tax shelters."

Pointing his finger at the printout, Jamie asked, "Would you suggest any major changes?"

At that point, the boat lurched violently to starboard. Theo stepped outside for a moment and gave Marcello a pointer. "You did say he'd had sailing lessons?" Theo said when he got back inside.

"They both did but this is a bigger boat than they're used to."

"Of course. Since we're on the topic of smooth sailing, this is why I prefer the Lazy ETF Portfolio, at least for the taxable portfolio. It's too stressful worrying about market turbulence and fretting about the fortunes of individual stocks."

"I can never get it straight how much to put in or where in the world to put it. Every time I travel in some exotic spot on business, I feel like I should invest there."

Theo looked amused and barked out another instruction for Marcello. When he turned his attention back to Jamie, he said, "Geographical mix? That's not too tough. You're still comfortable with a 60/40 asset mix?"

"Yes. 60% stocks to 40% bonds seems about right to me, though when the market's dumping I'd prefer it were the other way around." Little frown lines creased Jamie's tanned forehead as he thought about market volatility.

"Keep it simple then. You're no longer restricted by the amount of foreign content that can be held in registered plans, so the world is your oyster. You can get global equity exposure through just three ETFs from Vanguard or Barclays Global: 20% the United States, 20% Canada and 20% international, perhaps with a dash of Emerging Markets."

"Victor has most of his money in the U.S."

"Of course. It makes sense for Americans to overweight their own economy, and the U.S. still makes up almost half of the world's stock market capitalization. Canada is only about 4%, with the economy exposed to just three main sectors."

"Energy is one of them, I know that."

"Right, plus financials and raw materials. You need to look elsewhere for pharmaceuticals, manufacturing, software and other key sectors. Any broad-based U.S. or international ETF will give you that."

Theo was foraging about in the refrigerator again. "How about something a little stronger?" He pulled out a half-bottle of California Chardonnay.

Jamie gave him the thumbs up as Theo cracked open the bottle and poured generous measures into two tall clear plastic wine glasses. He continued his discourse. "Several academic studies—notably from Eugene Fama and Ken French—have shown that over the long term there is a little extra return from value and small-cap equities. You can get that through the enhanced index funds of Dimensional Fund Advisors or certain ETFs from Claymore or Wisdom Tree."

"What about currency?" Jamie asked. "I get worried when the U.S. and Canadian dollars fall out of sync."

"I consider currency an asset class, too though not all advisors do. Once your foreign holdings exceed 25% you should find products that hedge back into your local currency: Canadian in your case, American in the case of your brother."

"How do you do that?"

"In your case, you could buy a Barclays ETF that uses futures contracts to provide exposure to the S&P500 index. Unlike a 'pure' U.S. equity fund, it would be denominated in Canadian dollars. That portion of your portfolio would be less exposed to movements in the U.S. dollar."

"Do you do that for fixed income too?"

"Some people like foreign bonds. I think you should just keep the 40% fixed-income allocation in local bonds. If you want to take risks with foreign securities, at least get paid for it by using equities. Keep the strip bond laddered out and you'll be fine."

"Sheena always asks me what laddering means. I'm never quite sure how I should describe it."

"Tell her it just means you stagger maturities. One bond matures a year from now, another two years from now, a third three years from now. Each time one matures, just reinvest at whatever the going interest rate is. You could have them staggered over five to ten years. With today's relatively flat yield curve, you may even want to use GICs and keep the longest maturity to no more than two years."

Outside, the wind was blowing harder and some waves were crashing over the prow. One of them soaked Michaela. When she squealed indignantly, Jamie had to laugh.

"We also worry about inflation," Jamie said when he turned his attention back to the spreadsheet.

"Who doesn't? Equities handle that normally, since most quality stocks over time increase their dividends faster than inflation. Some believe real estate and gold can also hedge against inflation if western governments abuse their power and resort to printing too much paper money."

Jamie laughed. "Fiat money. Like Zimbabwe's 100-billion-dollar note that buys two loaves of bread."

"Same thing happened in Weimar Germany," Theo grinned. "They used wheel-barrows full of marks to buy food. One guy let his barrow out of his sight and someone stole it. The thief just left the worthless paper money in a pile on the ground. The barrow itself had more value."

"One of the gold bugs at Vinyl Nation swears bonds will be worthless one day."

"He has a point, but if you're really worried about inflation, buy inflation-linked Real Return Bonds. If inflation soars beyond the 2% or 3% a year that most govern-ments try to hold it to, you'll be glad you bought them. Say, god forbid, inflation soared to 10% one year. Then the government—it's governments that issue these mostly—would be on the hook to pay you the extra interest proportional to the difference between the 3% and the 10%."

Jamie looked out at Marcello and frowned. "Marco's been doing a good job but I think he could use a break."

They started to clamber out of the cabin.

"Sheena keeps badgering me about buying real estate."

"A rental stream of income is always nice," Theo said, ducking his head through the cabin door, "as long as you don't mind being a landlord."

"You speak from experience?"

"Did I never tell you we have two investment properties? Ariana plays the role of rent collector and landlord."

"So she's the one that put the idea in Sheena's head."

"Wouldn't be surprised."

Jamie went up to Marcello and patted him on the back. "Super job, son. Want a break?"

"Wouldn't mind, dad." He gave up the rudder to his father.

"There's some sodas in the refrigerator," Theo said. "Help yourself."

As Marcello descended to the cabin, Jamie yelled, "And don't forget to get one for your sister."

With his eye on the horizon, Jamie said to Theo, "What if we borrowed to buy real estate?"

"Many fortunes have been built that way, but at your stage I'm not sure I'd go that route. Real estate is such a cyclical business. You'd be concentrating your capital in one or two very specific properties in one location. That's why I like REITs."

"Sheena wants real bricks and mortar. To tell you the truth, I was thinking I'd use conservative leverage and borrow $60,000 to buy a broadly based U.S. equity ETF while the market has come off its highs. Al is always telling me about his great leveraged deals and how well he does. I wouldn't mind some of the same. Besides, if the market takes off again I could take profits and buy Sheena her real estate."

Theo looked dubious. "Could work, though it smacks of market timing. Personally, I'm opposed to it. I believe it's impossible to predict short-term moves in the stock market or interest rates, real estate or commodities for that matter."

"What counts is time in the market, not timing the market," Jamie said.

The skies were darkening. The waves were getting rougher. Jamie struggled to keep the boat on an even keel.

"You've been reading!" said Theo. "Still, the U.S. has been down so long, it's got to bounce back eventually. Better than investing in asset classes that have been the top performers for the last five years."

"Like emerging markets."

"Yes, or commodities. Personally, the way the market's been lately, I wouldn't borrow to invest. But it's not me that implements your trades, and I'm a generation older than you. You're a big boy now. You have to make your own financial decisions."

"I am," Jamie said, as a drop of rain spattered against his face. Michaela retreated to the cabin. Jamie adjusted course.

"I'm prepared for some turbulence in the stock markets, but I think it's time to turn this puppy back to shore."

■ ■ ■

Their finances were in solid enough shape that the banker approved an investment loan on the spot. Jamie put two-thirds of the borrowed $60,000 into a U.S. exchange-traded fund. Seeking the supposed safety of diversification, he invested the remaining one-third in an international large-cap ETF.

As summer gave way to autumn, the financial newspapers were filled with dire retrospectives about past stock market crashes that had occurred during the month of October. From the Crash of '29 to the significant correction of 1987, it was white-knuckle time.

Jamie was particularly nervous after committing to his leveraged loan in the teeth of what now appeared to be a vicious bear market. He began to have second thoughts about his rash move, but as the markets slipped, there was little he could do about it.

Sure enough, on the Monday before the month ended, the Dow Jones Industrial Average plunged 30%, taking all global stock markets down with it. Over breakfast the next morning, Sheena pointed to the front-page headlines. "Are we affected?"

Jamie had hoped to surprise her when his leveraged loan paid off and he parlayed the profits into real estate. Now he had to 'fess up. The thought of Sheena's reaction made him almost as nervous as the headlines.

"Sure, everyone's affected," he tried to appear nonchalant. "Big pension funds, small investors, just about anyone who doesn't have all his money hidden away in a mattress."

"Or who was short the market."

"Right," Jamie squirmed. "I didn't know you were such a sophisticated investor." The cereal tasted like dust in his dry mouth. He winked at Marcello, who was wolfing down his cereal, seemingly oblivious to its bland taste. "Where's your sister this morning?"

"Sleepover," Marcello grunted. "Sorry dad, got to run. Soccer practice."

"Need a lift?"

"It's ok. Frank's dad is taking us."

Jamie nodded. When Marcello was out of earshot, he sighed.

Sheena picked up from where she'd left off. "I was saying, I'm not such a naïve investor as you seem to think. Remember that dinner at Theo's cottage, when we told him we'd reached his $250,000 minimum asset level?"

"Of course. Big day."

"Remember him telling us about hedging our portfolio, reverse index funds and reverse ETFs? They go up when the market goes down, in some cases by a factor of two."

"I know that, but that also means they go down when the market goes up. I've always believed stocks go up two-thirds of the time, so why bet against them falling?"

"Well they just did. At least we weren't leveraged."

"Um," Jamie reddened. "Actually we were." He glanced again at the newspaper that Sheena had placed on the breakfast table. He had a visceral reaction to the headline, "Plunge!" He folded the paper and tossed it into the recycle bin.

Sheena looked concerned. "We were leveraged? News to me. When did this happen? After one of your benders with Al?"

"No, hon, a few weeks ago, after I met with Theo."

"He agreed to it?"

"Not exactly," Jamie said, sheepishly. "He said he wouldn't do it himself, but I was a big boy now."

"Hope it wasn't much. Conservative leverage, right?" Sheena placed both hands on the back of the bar stool in their sunny kitchen, staring at her husband of twenty years.

He took another bite and sipped his coffee.

"It wasn't nothing, Sheena, I won't lie to you."

She raised her eyebrows in that 'so tell me already' mannerism she had perfected.

"60 grand," he said.

"Come again?"

"$60,000."

"I'm not hearing you. Did you say sixty thousand dollars of our hard-earned money?"

"Not precisely. Since we borrowed it, technically we haven't earned it yet."

"So we have to keep paying into it? We're back in debt?"

"For four years, yes. That's the way these things work." He raised his left hand and opened it, pursing his lips at the same time.

"I can't believe you could be so stupid," she said bitterly, "This is the last straw."

"Last straw?" He put down his spoon and looked her straight in the eye.

She returned his gaze with eyes blazing. "It was bad enough that you made me scrimp and save all those years. I could live with it, if it had actually paid off. But now you've wiped us out."

"We're not wiped out. It was less than 5% of our total net worth," he said, pausing to drain his orange juice. "It's not like the market has fallen to zero. It'll come back. It always has."

Sheena didn't look convinced. "That's the end of your bloody Findependence Day, isn't it?" she said. She walked over to flick on the stereo, punching in her favourite light classical station.

"It will be a challenge getting there the way things look now."

"Apart from your irresponsible gamble, were we exposed to the market in the rest of our investments?"

"Of course. The 40% in fixed income is a nice buffer, as are the REITs and gold funds. I won't sugarcoat it. We're likely down $100,000 on our total portfolio. But that would have happened even without the investment loan."

"A hundred thousand?" Sheena's face paled. "Plus the $60,000 you borrowed? My God, we're destitute."

"No, Sheena, we're not. It's a temporary setback. If anything, we should buy more while stocks are on sale."

"With what? Are you going to sell your pristine copies of *Surrealistic Pillow* and *The White Album*?"

"You're funny."

As the announcer on the radio began the 8 am news, they both fell silent. The

U.S. stock market was falling further, in sympathy with Asian markets that had fallen in reaction to the earlier decline in North America. Jamie didn't know which was worse: reading the word 'plunge' or hearing the phrase 'wipe out.'

"It's everywhere," Sheena said. "Like falling dominoes. And you were leveraged, like an idiot."

Jamie sighed as fear and guilt combined into righteous indignation. "Had the market soared you'd have thought I was a hero."

Sheena looked at him with contempt. "Not likely."

"Think I'll take a walk."

Jamie slammed the door behind him and headed for the nearby park, where the neighbours walked their dogs. The coffee churned in his stomach. He'd put on a brave show for Sheena, but he only half believed it. He passed newspapers in several boxes, all of which had splashed the calamity across their front pages, varying only in the point size of the type. They ranged from a simple "Crash!" to "Markets plummet," "Panic grips financial markets" and similar tales of woe.

My timing couldn't have been worse, he thought. *What was I thinking?*

The park itself was mercifully free of newspaper boxes, but Jamie couldn't escape the din of his own thoughts. Theo always told him to ignore the media—"Idiot Wind" he called it, cribbing from Bob Dylan—but these days it was hard to ignore the non-stop cacophony of all-news radio, 24-hour cable TV news shows and the world wide web. The talking heads had been gnashing their teeth about the crash ad nauseum for 24 hours straight. The more they did, the more they fuelled the growing hysteria of the average investor.

It could be ugly, Jamie thought. If this is the big one, there's no telling how low it goes. *Maybe Sheena's right. We should sell what we have left before it goes down further.*

Jamie had half a mind to run back to the house and put in a sell order at his online account, but he couldn't decide on the proper course of action. Maybe he should call Theo. When I decide these things myself, he thought, I have a fool for a client.

Theo had failed to talk him out of the leveraged loan, although Jamie had to admit that wasn't Theo's job. In the final analysis, no one knew anything. It was all just guesswork and luck. In his case, bad luck.

Jamie didn't even want to think about Findependence Day. Even without the leverage, being 60% in equities after the market fell 30% translated into an instant loss of more than 15%. Or was it 20%? One thing was clear. This one cruel act of the market gods was going to set him back a good five years, maybe more.

He could see himself now in old age. Still setting the alarm clock to go off at dawn, putting in his dentures and shuffling off to Wal-Mart for another day of greeting customers. Or, under the golden arches, "Would you like fries with that, sonny?"

Jamie wished he'd never heard the word stock. He should have invested in nothing but bonds and cash, like his old man. Not only should he never have touched stocks, he should never have tried to behave like a stock. He should have gone into teaching or worked for the government, joined their Defined Benefit pension plan and hung in for 30 years.

What was Sheena so worried about? She was sitting pretty, free and clear. Her Findependence Day was still on track and likely to happen before his. What a fool he was.

Then he remembered something Theo had said about portfolio targets. Jamie turned around, quickened his pace and returned home. He had to get online, and he had to do it now.

Chapter 13

Dedicated to the One I Love

[THE MAMAS & THE PAPAS, 1967]

O ver the next two years the market stabilized gradually and with it the Morelli marriage. In either case, a truce might be a more accurate descriptor. With the twins in high school, Jamie and Sheena tried to keep 38 Verdant Crescent a place of harmony. The market crack-up had put such a scare into him that Jamie seldom indulged in dreams of his financial future. His extensive travel obligations continued at Far East Electronica. He had little choice but to keep his nose to the grindstone.

The bright spot in his life was Vinyl Nation. Though not a huge moneymaker, his cyber-friends around the world were always supportive, even when his family and work associates were not. The Pop Culture and Money chat rooms attracted participants in increasing numbers. The more traffic and "eyeballs" they attracted the more he could charge for banner ads.

He regularly engaged in verbal repartee in the Pop Culture forum with someone who called himself Nimrod. They clashed swords over classic rock and the relative value of analog versus digital music, but Jamie had to admit the guy—or girl—knew his pop culture.

In the Money forum, a large gang of knowledgeable do-it-yourself investors, including Mr. Market, Seenitall and a new arrival called Boomerbucks, seemed to be broad generalists. Some even seemed to know plenty about his own consumer electronics industry.

Jamie's Classic Rock blog was cross-linked to so many other pop culture blogs that he'd become something of a minor celebrity in those circles. But it was only when he composed a seminal blog entry called *The Day the Music Died* that Vinyl Nation hit the radar screens of the arbiters of pop culture. The essay marked the point when Jamie became a key journalistic source for major broadcasters and the traditional print media.

His thesis was that the younger generation largely houses its music in ephemeral devices like portable MP3 players or on the hard disk drives of their desktop and laptop computers, all of which are replaced in a few years. Often, the music contained on them dies when the owners acquire a new computer or portable device. As for music residing on the web, it's almost as ephemeral as music sent by a radio station over the airwaves.

Jamie asked his readers to imagine a future dark age when the knowledge of how to retrieve music or video from laser disks was lost. Future archeologists digging through the detritus of our culture would find books they may or may not be able to decipher, like the Dead Sea scrolls. They would find strange shiny disks, but would know nothing about laser technology to retrieve the data. If instead they found vinyl records and old turntables, they might be able to figure out that a needle dragged across a vinyl groove would reproduce sounds. This was the basis of Jamie's call to action. Vinyl must be preserved or a way found to keep digital music more permanent.

Jamie composed this on his 47th birthday and posted it with no great expectation of changing his world or anyone else's.

Later in July, before the ripples of the post had become waves, the twins headed off to sleepover camp—"the best weeks of our lives," they said every summer—giving their parents a much-needed breather. Jamie and Sheena accepted an invitation to Theo's cottage three hours north of the city, an exclusive area bounded by rolling hills, streams and lakes. Since he'd become their official advisor, Theo had made this an annual event, despite the difference in the couples' ages.

Perhaps Ariana was some sort of substitute for Sheena's departed mother, Jamie speculated. Certainly, Theo loomed large in his own mind, a cross between an older brother and a father figure.

The cottage was located not on a lake but in secluded woodland. A river ran through the center of the property. "The ultimate income stream," Theo quipped, strolling with Jamie and Sheena after lunch one day. Except for a small area that Theo had cleared, most of the acreage was dense woodlot: white pines and hard maples.

"Nice of Ariana to do the dishes," Sheena said, cool and comfortable in faded cut-offs and a green t-shirt.

"I imagine she'll take the opportunity to have her nap," Theo replied.

"Could use one myself."

"I read the review of your second book," Theo said to Sheena. "You must be pleased."

"I am. I intend to do at least seven."

"Like J.K. Rowling."

"But without the billion dollars," Jamie quipped.

"Perhaps not," Sheena said, "but the royalties have become a welcome additional stream of income." There was still an edge to her tone whenever Jamie brought up the subject of money.

They'd reached the deep wide part of the stream in which Theo and Ariana often bathed. Jamie and Theo announced their intention to take a dip in the buff. Sheena opted to return to Ariana.

Jamie stepped down to a rock and into the shallow part of the stream, offering his hand to help Theo follow. When Sheena was out of earshot, Theo remarked on Sheena's evident irritation with him.

Jamie shrugged. "She's been that way ever since the market dumped after the leveraged loan."

"But stocks have been fighting their way back since. It can't have set you back more than a year or two from your goal."

"Perhaps not. Tell you the truth, I've stopped looking at the statements." He dipped his head into the stream and lathered his head with Ariana's homemade biodegradable soap, which she kept tucked between two rocks.

"A natural reaction. During bull markets, clients love to rip open their statements to verify their growing wealth. When stocks are falling, they won't even open them. A bit like ostriches laying their heads on the ground."

"I'm not sure humans are well equipped to deal with financial markets."

"They're not," Theo said, "or so the behavioural finance gurus tell us. We're irrationally exuberant during manias and unreasonably despondent during downturns. That's why the great investor Warren Buffett liked to talk about the manic-depressive character he called Mr. Market."

"Right. Mr. Market is always willing to buy your stocks when you're depressed and sell them to you when you're bullish."

"The late Sir John Templeton always counselled investors to sell at the moment of maximum optimism and buy at the moment of greatest pessimism." Theo submerged himself in the stream. When he resurfaced, he spluttered from the cold. "But of course," he continued, "Most investors do the opposite. It's just human nature."

"How do we deal with it then?"

"Strategic asset allocation is one way. I've always counselled the classic pension-fund split of 60% stocks to 40% bonds. If you're on the aggressive side you can move that to 70% stocks. If you're conservative you can be 50% stocks. But even the most timid retiree I'd still counsel to have a minimum 25% in blue-chip quality dividend-paying stocks."

"Spread out among the five main sectors of the economy."

"Right, or broadly diversified exchange-traded funds or reasonably priced mutual funds that are automatically spread across those sectors and others besides."

"Until the market scared me two years ago, I couldn't see why I shouldn't be 100% in stocks. I only added the 40% fixed income to placate Sheena. Of course, when it did fall, I was glad we'd gone the more conservative route."

Theo grabbed the soap, lathered his scalp and plunged into the stream again to rinse it off. Jamie listened to the gentle sound of the water where it splashed downstream over some rocks. He could hear the frogs from a nearby pond.

"It's true," Theo said when he re-emerged, "that over the very long haul, stocks outperform bonds, cash and other assets by a considerable margin." He shook his head to clear the water from his eyes. "But in the long run, we're all dead. There have been periods when stocks went nowhere for a decade and a half."

"They'd still pay dividends."

"True, and the compounding that provides is a major element of total return. That plus the steady returns from fixed income should be enough to keep investors from panicking. But there's another concept you should know about. Ever hear the term Asset Dedication?"

"Same thing as asset allocation?"

"Similar but different, which confuses many clients. There's a whole book on the subject by Stephen Huxley[11]. I mentioned this to you two years ago when you turned 45. Now you're within five years of your goal, you should start thinking about it seriously. Ever hear the phrase 'Retirement Risk Zone'?"

"Yes. It's used by the same finance professor who wrote about whether people are stocks or bonds." Jamie paused to search his mind for the name, "Milevsky, that's it."

Theo nodded approvingly.

"Right. So you know that the five years just preceding retirement and the five years following it are potentially hazardous?"

"Depending what the stock market does. It all depends on when the market rises and falls."

"It's called sequence-of-return risk. If the market falls just as you enter the zone, and you keep adding new money at better prices, you might do better. But if the market keeps rising as you enter the zone, and you buy at ever more expensive prices and it falls right at the end, that could be devastating. Findependence Day could be pushed back several years."

Jamie grimaced. "Don't I know it! That's what I figured happened when it crashed two years ago."

"That may have been a dress rehearsal. With Asset Dedication, you dedicate a portion of your portfolio to, say, fixed income."

Theo was drying himself off. "Say you absolutely must have $50,000 a year to live on. Because we know that under five years, stocks can go down, once you're in the risk zone you want to absolutely guarantee you'll have $50,000 a year for at least those five years. So how much would you have to dedicate to cash or bonds?"

"$50,000 times five, which is $250,000. Enough to become your client!" Then Jamie added, "But that's breaking into capital. 5% of $250,000 is only $12,500 a year. Hardly the same thing as $50,000."

"Right, but don't forget we also have stocks and dividend income. Now let's say you have ten times as much money: $2.5 million. But you still can live on the same $50,000. How much would you dedicate to bonds?"

Jamie leant his chin on his hand and made some mental calculations. "Under asset dedication I guess the same $250,000, with the other $2.25 million in stocks."

"So you see how different it is from asset allocation. With standard asset allocation, you'd have 40% of the $2.5 million in bonds, which is $1 million. With Asset Dedication you dedicate the minimum you need to achieve your income goals."

They began walking back to the cottage. Over the years a defined route had been established through the small rocks and plants that littered their path.

"I see," Jamie said. "Even though in this case you didn't need it all."

"With asset dedication, you put all the difference in stocks: the growth potential in the part of the portfolio you won't need to touch for at least five years. Eventually,

[11]See appendix, A Peek at Theo's Library

assuming the long-term growth of the market comes through for you, you'll have plenty more capital. And if your standard of living rises as a result, you can decide to dedicate more to the bond part."

"So if I decide we need at least $100,000 a year for five years, we'd dedicate $500,000 to the fixed-income portion."

"Correct. The point is that if you only had $500,000, you'd have to dedicate the whole amount to bonds if $100,000 a year was your nut. Under normal asset allocation, you'd have $300,000 of that in stocks. But with asset dedication, once you've taken care of the guaranteed safe money, the amount dedicated to stocks may soar, well past the limits asset allocation would dictate, as your wealth grows."

By the time they reached the cottage, Ariana had some cocktails ready. They sat down to drink them on the flagstone terrace.

"You were gone awhile," Sheena said.

"I was learning about asset dedication," said Jamie.

Theo recapped the gist of the lesson. Sheena said, "Good. I've been thinking I'd like to dedicate my money and Jamie's money in separate pots."

Jamie looked at her in surprise. "Honey, we've always mingled the money in our joint chequing account and our non-registered portfolios. You're going to have your pension and government benefits and withdrawals from your registered plan in your name anyhow. You think you're going to wake up one day and find that I'd transferred all our joint assets to some offshore account?"

"Stranger things have happened," Sheena said. "Remember how Eamon abused the joint bank account he had with my mother?"

Jamie shrugged, giving Theo a "What did I say?" look.

■ ▩ ▨

Almost from the beginning of his career, the January consumer electronics show in Las Vegas was a must event for Al Peters. The massive trade show sprawled across acres of a modern convention centre situated conveniently next to one of the biggest casinos.

The show was the perfect blend of business and pleasure. By day, Al networked with influential industry executives from around the world. By night, the gambling, celebrity shows and women were an intoxicating tonic. He never slept much in Vegas.

This year, beginning with a press conference on the first day of the show, Al hoped to leverage Jamie's expanding circle of media contacts to plant favourable stories in the west-coast technology press and blogosphere about Far East Electronica. It had taken three long years, but the company's public offering was fast approaching. The Las Vegas show would also mark the first of many dog-and-pony events for the investment analysts covering the industry.

Al had insisted that bloggers and mainstream media should all attend the same press conference. He had waved aside Jamie's objections that the financial press and stock analysts should have a separate briefing focused on the public offering. "The more of them, the more the publicity," Al had reasoned.

Al knew the steady stream of journalists and bloggers filing in to the media room this morning were there primarily because of Jamie. He was glad he'd stuck with him all these years.

At one o'clock, Al kicked off the press conference, sailing through the financial content without a hitch. Then he passed the microphone to Jamie for a recap of the product line and marketing plans.

When they threw it open for questions, a stock analyst asked Al to explain some footnotes in the preliminary prospectus. Al's response seemed to satisfy that group. A reporter from one of the big financial newspapers questioned the timing of the offering, but again Al felt satisfied he'd skated through it with no major faux pas.

Then a scruffy middle-aged man in the front row stood up, intent on asking a question. He had a scraggly grey beard, was badly in need of a hair cut, and his shoes were down at heel. Al recognized him as Philippe Nimard, a notorious video blogger. Some weeks before, Jamie had confided to Al that Nimard had become one of his rivals, even co-opting Jamie's retro culture shtick with his own popular video blog, Dinosaur Media.

Al looked at him with distaste. The man had no understanding of the concept of dressing for success. But with no other questions on the floor, Al could no longer ignore him.

With exaggerated self-importance, Nimard waved a pen in the air and asked, "What's the connection between Far East Electronica and Vinyl Nation?"

Al glanced at Jamie, indicating it was his question to respond to.

"None really," Jamie replied. "I'm an executive at FEE, which imports electronics from, as our name implies, the Far East. Vinyl Nation is a hobby Internet site that I run, increasingly with the help of other members of the community."

"Are they paid?"

"No. You could call them volunteers. We share an interest in preserving the rich heritage engendered by the music that historians will one day revere as the vinyl era."

"Fending off the day the music dies?" Nimard said.

Al knew that was a reference to Jamie's seminal blog posting that had pushed Vinyl Nation to critical mass. The essay compared the community to the monks who kept key doctrines in print during the middle ages.

Nimard produced a video camera and began to tape Jamie's comments. Al smiled as Jamie took the opportunity to launch into his vinyl preservation spiel.

"That's right," Jamie said. "We have a long-term perspective on preserving the culture. We believe future generations will look back on the vinyl era as the golden age of popular music. Our children's children's children will still be listening to this music, just as we today listen to the immortal classics conceived by Bach and Mozart three hundred years ago."

"Far East Electronica now supplies turntables and needles?" Nimard persisted.

Al noticed Jamie was temporarily at a loss for words.

"That's true," he replied. "There was a gap in the market we saw could be filled."

"So there *is* a connection between the two enterprises," Nimard cried triumphantly.

"Yes, but it's a tiny piece of the business. FEE is primarily about future media, not dinosaur media. You of all people should know that, Phillipe."

"I assume this will all be properly disclosed in the prospectus," Nimard persisted.

At that point Al stepped in. "That's all the time we have for questions," he said. "We only have the room for half an hour. If anyone wants a one-on-one with Jamie or myself we can arrange it. Please help yourself to refreshments. All are welcome at the hospitality suite tonight."

"Watch him," Jamie said under his breath. "He fancies himself the master of 'gotcha' journalism."

A few hours later, Nimard showed up at FEE's hospitality suite and captured more footage. Al chatted with him briefly, but there were far more important industry people and financial analysts at the suite, not to mention more attractive ones.

One was Candy, a showgirl and ex-girlfriend he'd pressured into serving hors d'oeuvres. "What time is your show?" he asked, munching on a canapé.

"8 pm," she smiled. "You'll be in one of the front tables as usual?"

"Wouldn't miss it," Al said. "Have you met my associate, Jamie Morelli?"

"Enchantée," Candy said. She offered her arm as a gag, and in a mock gesture of gallantry Jamie planted a kiss on it. When he looked up, he saw Nimard. "What's he doing here?" Jamie said.

Nimard had elbowed his way through the crowd, videotaping the proceedings as he went. Al shooed him away but a few hours later, when Candy started her show at the casino, Nimard was there again. It was a provocative act, even for Al's liberal tastes. Candy was well endowed, and her low-slung black dress left little to the imagination. Al loved the scene: the beautiful women, the glitz, the glamour of a Vegas show.

Jamie was enjoying the show as well, not least because Al made sure a regular flow of doubles arrived at the table. By the time these morphed into triples, Jamie was in no condition to notice the difference.

At the end of the show, Candy visited the table. She chucked Al under the chin. "Shall I come up to the suite for a nightcap, lover?" she said, glancing at Jamie, who was struggling to remain upright in his chair. "He's cute," she said. "You should bring him too."

"Oh, I intend to," Al said.

When Al had settled the tab, they took the elevator up to the suite, where the booze continued to flow.

"Where's Cinderella?" Al asked one of the guests.

"In the bedroom, changing."

"Not into glass underwear, I hope," Al smirked.

At that moment, a familiar figure entered the suite "Philippe," Al said. He gave him a friendly smile. "Welcome. Have a drink." He indicated the bar.

The look on his face told Al that Jamie was not happy to see Nimard again or the equipment that followed him everywhere. Jamie knocked back another drink but was unsteady on his feet.

"Easy, boy," Al steadied him. "I think you need a nap." He guided Jamie to the bedroom and knocked. Without waiting for a response, he opened the door. Candy was still in her bra and panties but didn't seem perturbed by the intrusion. "Park him there, lover." Jamie staggered to the bed and was unconscious by the time his head hit the pillow.

Al didn't see Nimard's face again for the rest of the evening. But the next morning, an assistant startled him awake with an urgent phone call to his hotel suite. He directed Al to Nimard's latest clip airing on YouTube.

After he'd watched it once, Al knocked on the door of the adjoining suite where Jamie was still sound asleep. "Come right away," Al said. "You have to see what Nimard has posted. A million hits and rising."

The clip was only a minute long, but it couldn't have been more damaging.

"What a sleazeball!" Jamie said, after he'd dragged himself out of bed.

He crowded closer to the monitor. Nimard had begun the segment with the press conference, noting the corporate connection between Jamie's web site and FEE. Then he jumped to the moment Jamie kissed Candy's hand and from there to the hotel room with Candy in her shiny black underwear, leaning over the bed where Jamie lay.

"He sandbagged you."

Jamie's face was ashen, but he tried to downplay it. "It's only Nimard. No one takes his blog videos that seriously."

Al pursed his lips. "I'm not so sure about that. The clip's being picked up everywhere. It seems your journalistic buddies are more than happy to give you this kind of exposure."

Al flipped on the TV in the hotel room and surfed the channels. Sure enough, a brief portion of the clip was airing on a few local stations, which were covering the electronics show and using the clip as a humorous segment in the midst of more serious technological news.

"The glass is at least half full," Al said. "Everyone on the west coast now knows about Far East Electronica."

"It's the half-empty part that worries me," Jamie said.

■ ■ ■

When he walked through the front door of 38 Verdant Crescent a few days later, Jamie had almost forgotten the video incident, as he called it. It was generally acknowledged—certainly on the Vinyl Nation discussion forums—that Nimard had been unethical in the way he had spliced his video together.

Unfortunately, Sheena was not as receptive an audience as the Vinyl Nation community. There was no hug to greet Jamie, although they'd been rather rare the last few years anyhow. No supper on the table either.

"I figured you'd eat on the plane."

"I did. A nourishing bag of potato chips. I'll put a frozen pizza in the oven." She was glowering at him.

"Something bothering you?"

"You think millions of YouTube viewers watching my husband in bed with a Las Vegas tart should bother me?"

"That was just Nimard. He's been gunning for me ever since Vinyl Nation took off."

"That's not how our friends see it. I can't tell you how many embarrassing phone calls I've received about this. I can barely show my face in the staff room at school. Before I enter, there's the normal buzz of chatter. Then when they see me suddenly you can hear a pin drop."

"It'll blow over."

"I think not," Sheena said, her voice cracking.

"I can't believe you'd fall for that sleazy journalistic hatchet job," Jamie said, in a voice that combined indignation and despair, "He's a professional rival. He did everything he could to make me look bad."

"And he succeeded," Sheena said, her face flush with anger and hurt. "I'll say this much. She's gifted."

"I'd never met the woman before. We were clowning around."

"I know. Before a nationwide audience."

"I knew I shouldn't have invited Nimard."

"Why did you?" Her voice was pleading, seemingly ready to forgive.

"I was trying to rack up the media body count to impress Al," Jamie said. "Every little bit of coverage helps."

"You certainly got the coverage," she said, with a hint of sarcasm.

"It was an error in judgement. His motivation was clear. Some misguided notion that by tearing me down he could build himself up."

Her nose wrinkled up in disgust. "He's certainly an ugly little man."

"He's a disgrace. I wouldn't give him any further thought."

He put a frozen pizza into the oven and fetched a beer from the refrigerator. When he rejoined Sheena in the living room, she was staring out the picture window, deep in thought.

"You see, Jamie," she began, turning back to face him, "I *have* been giving him further thought. Or more to the point, giving *us* further thought."

Jamie slumped in the couch and flipped off the beer cap with a smooth jerk of the opener.

"Nimard is only the tip of the iceberg," Sheena continued. "If that's how you behave in front of the media, God only knows what you do behind closed doors. You and Al in the casinos. I can see it now."

She bit her lip and turned away, running her left hand through her hair. Jamie could see the light from the chandelier glinting off her wedding ring.

"We only went once. A bit of roulette for a few hours. It was 90% business."

She whirled to face him, her face flushed with anger.

"It's the other 10% that bothers me. I don't think I can trust you any more."

"Trust me? We've been married 23 years."

"And what I don't know *can* hurt me. What do they say, What happens in Vegas stays in Vegas?"

"That's a marketing line, nothing more."

"I wish I could believe you," she said, almost plaintively.

"You can. Trust me."

"That's just it. The trust is gone. You travel all around the world, half the time with that man. I've never liked him. He's a bad influence on you."

Jamie patted the couch cushion next to him, beckoning her to sit beside him, but Sheena remained standing.

"Al's my employer. How can he be a bad influence? If we play our cards right, his company could be our ticket to freedom."

"You never spend time with us anymore. You're hardly there for Micki and Marco. You forget my birthday. It took three days of hints before I got you to remember our anniversary."

Jamie sat red-faced, suddenly ashamed. But she hadn't finished.

"And when you're not cavorting with Al or Theo, you're talking to people you've never even met on your web site."

"I've met many of them on my business trips."

"I'm sure you have." Then, as if the light had suddenly dawned, she said, "How many are female?"

Jamie didn't like the tone in her voice, which was a mix of defiance and sarcasm. He'd heard that tone a lot the last six months. "Come on, Sheena. You know better than that." He got up from the couch but kept his distance.

"Do I? I'm not sure any more. One thing I can tell you. When you do reach Findependence Day, you're not going to like it. You're going to have nothing but time on your hands and no one to share it with."

"I don't think so. It's potentially a life-altering event. It's not the end. It's the beginning of a major new chapter in our lives. As Bryan Adams once sang, 'the best is yet to come.'"

She raised her eyes to the ceiling, a habit he figured she'd picked up from Michaela. "Do you have to keep throwing song lyrics at me? We're talking about our future together, and you try to reduce it all to a song title?"

"I happen to find it relevant …" Jamie's voice tailed off as he averted his gaze, glancing out the window.

"I don't. I've never shared your interest in dinosaur rock. As a matter of fact, I could care less about music in general. To me, silence is—"

"Golden," Jamie finished for her, grinning. "Put your arms around me." He tried to sing a bar of the Tremeloes hit, was practically willing her to embrace him in return and forgive him.

Sheena backed away. "Don't touch me."

She walked a few steps to her purse, which was lying on the table by the front door. She extracted a brown envelope and, grimly, handed it to Jamie.

"I've had these for six months, Jamie," she said, her eyes blazing with anger. "Now they're yours."

He opened the envelope. It was a legal document. Jamie recognized the letterhead. The same firm had prepared their wills and powers of attorney.

He blinked as he read the first few sentences.

Re: *Morelli v. Morelli—Matrimonial*

We write as the solicitors for your wife Sheena Morelli. We request you take this letter to a Family Law lawyer immediately and have your lawyer contact me on an urgent basis to resolve the following matters:

1. Separation
   Your wife advises...

Chapter 14

It's Over

[JIMMIE RODGERS, 1966]

Jamie read the solicitor's demand letter, staring in disbelief at the pages clutched in his hands. All he was seeing was words on paper. He could no longer decipher their meaning. He began to function on autopilot, mumbled something about needing to take a drive and brushed past Sheena. He entered the garage and turned the ignition on the Prius.

For a moment, he just sat there, whitened fingers gripping the wheel. He activated the garage door opener, not knowing his destination. But any place was better than 38 Verdant Crescent at this moment of his life.

He pulled out of the driveway at normal speed and took the first right. At the next intersection he did the same and continued to do so at every major intersection thereafter. Soon he was in farm country.

He wasn't quite sure it had happened at all. "How could such a thought have entered her mind?" he wondered. And when?

Jamie thought back to the last few years. Now and then she had dropped a few hints. But it was always in the context of "if things don't get better" on such and such a front. Travel. Money. The Twins. The web site. Al. Sheena wanted balance, and Jamie thought he'd delivered it.

When he thought about Nimard his anger bubbled up again over that ridiculous video. It was all so trumped up, like his firing from Tech Heaven.

He took a series of deep breaths, trying to dispel the pain building up in his chest. Was it imaginary or real? Was a broken heart more than just a metaphor? What had happened to this sweet Irish lass who had become the mother of his children, his life companion, his soul mate? When he thought of their future together, the picture was always of two old folks sitting on a porch, rocking their chairs together before the sunset, gnarled hand in gnarled hand. And the years from now until that sunset were to be the best of their lives.

"How could she do this to us?" he wondered. The best was yet to come!

Involuntarily, his mind scanned his cerebral jukebox and as always came up with just the right selection. That's it, he thought. Jimmy Ruffin.

Jamie reached for his melancholy car-mix CD, one of many he'd prepared for various moods. He punched in track 4: "What Becomes of the Broken Hearted?" The song played on as his thoughts drifted to other topics.

In purely financial terms, this was a major setback to the plan. Theo had always told him the biggest financial mistake his clients ever made was divorce. They'd have to sell 38 Verdant Crescent and move separately into two smaller homes. Their financial assets would be cut in half. The kids would be traumatized.

He thought of Woody Allen's quip that humans should mate for life, like pigeons. Financially, the pigeons—or was it penguins?—had it right.

Sheena had warned him more than once that "marriage is not a financial plan." He'd replied with something flippant, like "but two incomes are better than one and best of all are two pensions."

Now Jamie felt the anger build. How could she even think of separation?

He pulled in to a gas station to fill up. Nice little town, he thought. *I could pull up stakes and set up shop here.* Next to him, an attractive young redhead was filling up. I could meet someone like her, he thought. Start all over. But Jamie had already met his redheaded soul mate decades ago, the only hot-tempered Irish lass he'd ever desired.

The woman caught his glance, smiled. Jamie returned it, finished the fill-up and pulled out, faster than normal. Like I'm in a hurry to get anywhere, he thought.

At the next intersection, he pulled off the main highway and took a dirt road that seemed to be leading to a body of water. He could take his half of the proceeds from 38 Verdant Crescent, buy a little lakefront property in a place like this, kick back and make a serious go of the web site.

Never mind waiting two more years, he could do it right now. "Findependence 47!" he cried. Now he was exhilarated. There was nothing but potential out there, the great unmanifest void ready to bend to his will.

Phrases from every motivational book he'd ever read popped uninvited into his mind. Yes I can! Think and Grow Rich. The Power of Positive Thinking. He would triumph over all who opposed him, go on to glory.

Then the manic mood that had gripped him vanished as quickly as it had come.

What about the kids? He couldn't go too far if he wanted to stay in contact with Marco and Micki. Would they stay with Sheena? Was he going to become one of those cliché "every second weekend" fathers? As he thought of his son and daughter, his gut started to feel queasy again. His freedom fantasy was an entertaining reverie while it lasted, but it would take many long years to realize, if it was realistic at all. Sell the house in a down market, wrangle with lawyers, all while maintaining Al's gruelling travel schedule?

Get real, he told himself. In the short term, he'd have to rent an apartment near Sheena, if only for the sake of the kids.

Did he really want to do that, though? Throwing money at landlords at this stage of his life? Now he wished he'd listened to Sheena and bought some rental unit instead of throwing his money away on the stock market. Worst case, he could have lived in the unit himself.

His melancholy mix CD had ended. Jamie searched among the scattered titles on the passenger seat for a replacement. He spied another mix he'd converted from some of his most cherished albums, the ones from his early visits to Bernie.

His thoughts drifted to the Vinyl Cave. Then he was hit with a brainstorm. "That's it!" he thought. He pulled a U-Turn and started back. He shifted down and with a silent thank-you for whoever invented hands-free mobile phone technology, placed a call to the Vinyl Cave.

"Bernie, Jamie here. Is that apartment still available to rent?"

Nodding, a smile beginning to form on his grim face, Jamie listened to Bernie. Then he said, "It's a long story, man. Can you just hold it for me for while? I'll drop in with a cheque next week."

No longer dawdling, Jamie stepped on the gas pedal.

■ ■ ■

It wasn't the ideal location for a carefree bachelor life, but the apartment over the Vinyl Cave fit with a new plan slowly forming in Jamie's mind. He'd arrived home from a three-week Asia stint to find his personal effects boxed and ready to go. Sheena was determined to make a change. Her angry last words still rang in his ears: "You're never here for me or the kids. We won't even see a difference, except now your stuff won't be here either."

Ikea was delivering everything he'd need for the apartment that afternoon, right down to the mattresses and pillows. He could haul the rest of his possessions in the Prius and a small U-Haul trailer.

It was a typically depressing day in February. As he drove through the slush, he silently sang Supertramp's *Lover Boy*: "He took a small apartment, above a shoe department."

The first thing he did when he got there was hook up his stereo.

Al surprised him by showing up to help carry the boxes of books and clothes. When he carried the first load up the single flight of stairs, he put down the box and glanced at the almost-empty unit. "This place is a dump."

Clearly, Bernie had not believed in pumping his meagre profits back into renovating his properties. The place was built soon after WWII and looked it. There was one tiny bedroom and a cramped kitchen with a couple of badly stained white Frigidaire appliances from the 50s. The living room had a little elbow room, but the wallpaper had begun to fray at the edges. One grimy window overlooked busy Lakefront Boulevard. The noise from the traffic and streetcars never let up.

"It's just temporary," Jamie replied. "Bernie agreed to let me rent it month by month in case my circumstances change."

"Nice guy."

"He is. But there's more to it than that. I'm thinking I could do a deal with him involving his business and the whole building."

"I get it," Al said, as the two descended the stairs for another load. "Vinyl Cave, Vinyl Nation."

"Something like that. We haven't hammered out the details, but Bernie's health isn't the greatest. All those years smoking God knows what has finally got to his lungs. He's always nixed previous offers to sell out, including mine, but now I think he's more receptive to the idea."

When they were outside, they unloaded a couple of suitcases from the trailer and climbed the stairs again.

"How much would he sell for?"

When Jamie told him, Al whistled. "You have that kind of money?"

"Getting there. Our credit's good for the rest."

"You get half the house?"

"Yep. Sheena's put it up for sale, but for now she's still living there with the twins."

"Exciting to be starting over again. In some ways I envy you."

Al was out of breath by the time they returned to the apartment. "Let's sit down for a minute." He sat on the stacked boxes of vinyl and books.

"It's the best thing that could happen to you," Al continued. "If I were single, what a party. Just dial up whatever you want on the Internet."

"I hadn't noticed that marriage had slowed you down that way," Jamie said, as he too sat down.

"Sure but it's still constraining. Betty is giving me a hard time. You're sitting pretty. You can be the only rooster in the henhouse." He paused, glancing around the apartment. "Of course, you'll have to fix this up. Better yet, make your pile and find a real place to live."

"I'm working on it."

"Wait till the IPO goes through and you can have any girl you want."

"Al, this is a trial separation. Sheena's my life partner. My work is to get her back."

"Forget her. After throwing you out over that harmless video?"

"It was more than that. Besides, I'd hardly call it harmless."

"Au contraire. That little publicity stunt put Far East Electronica on the map. It certainly got the attention of the underwriting guys. When they saw all the coverage, they decided to add $2 to the issue price."

"So Nimard actually made you money?"

"That's the size of it," Al said. "And he made a little for you, too. Remember, glass half full."

Jamie's cell phone buzzed.

"Hi Theo," he said when he answered. "We're at the apartment. You know where it is, right above the Vinyl Cave. I'll tell you when you get here."

"Your financial advisor?" Al said when Jamie closed his phone.

"And friend. He said he'd drop by with some beer."

Al rose from the chair. "Better get another load then so we'll earn it."

They made six more trips. When Jamie retrieved the last items from his car, Al suggested it was time he got a new one.

"It's a company car. You know that."

"Sure," Al nodded in the direction of his own Audi TTT parked next to Jamie's car. "But you should get a sports car too. Build up your image."

"I'll think about it," Jamie said, glancing down the street as Theo pulled up to the curb. "Speaking of nice cars."

Theo got out of his classic maroon Jaguar, carrying a carton of 12 bottles from a local microbrewery. "Wasn't sure you'd have an opener." He held up a branded vinyl-coated model from the Beer Store.

Upstairs, Theo was no more impressed than Al by Jamie's apartment. Al stayed for another few minutes, quickly downed a beer, then made his escape, just as Jamie and Theo began assembling the Ikea furniture.

"So that's the great Al Peters," Theo laughed. He ripped open the first box and pulled out the assembly instructions.

"That's him. Now he wants me to buy a new sports car to impress the chicks."

"Is that what you want too?"

"No way. In the best of all worlds, Sheena and I patch up our differences."

"And the worst?"

"I'm not thinking of the worst. Sheena is. Guess we might have to sell our house. One option would be to buy this building. Down the line, if things work out with the IPO, maybe I'd buy a cottage in the country."

"Will Bernie sell?"

"Think so, with a reasonable offer."

"Makes sense. If you owned the whole building, you'd have a significant asset. Commercial real estate can only get more valuable, especially in this central location. How many tenants here?"

"Two other businesses lease units on the ground floor," Jamie said. "Each has an apartment above."

He scribbled some figures on the back of the Ikea instruction sheet. "This district has never made it to the City's Top 50 Trendy Neighbourhoods list," he said. "But with the new condos going up, it just might take off."

Theo scrutinized the numbers, nodding approvingly.

"It's a decent plan. If it works you'll have as many streams of income as Ariana and me. But I'm not quite sure how you'd integrate the Vinyl Cave with Vinyl Nation."

"Vinyl Cave is a retail business with physical property, right?"

"Yes."

"Vinyl Nation is a web site."

"Go on."

"So it's clicks and bricks. The clicks represent a growing online community, with chapters around the world."

"But the bricks are just local. This one location."

"One location now, but what if it were franchised?"

"You *are* thinking big."

"Ray Kroc was in his 60s when he put McDonald's into the big time."

"Sure but that was another time and place," Theo said. "Do you really think some old record store selling obsolete media is a franchisable idea?"

Jamie's face dropped. "Not so good, huh?"

"It's not for me to say, but as your financial advisor, I'd say walk before you run. Get the deal done with Bernie and see how it works at this one location."

"That's my plan but it doesn't hurt to look down the road and see the potential. Think big, you always told me."

"I'm not retracting it. I just want you to focus on the deal at hand first. What exactly do you have in mind?"

"I see a total renovation of the Vinyl Cave. The business next door is already a low-end coffee shop. We let its lease expire, knock down the wall between us and open up a high-end Internet café."

"Like a vinyl Starbucks with banks of computer terminals?"

"Sort of. Right now, Vinylheads come to Bernie's to find a few LPs, buy new needles or refurbished turntables or to source nostalgia items. If they had an upscale café next door, they could relax, network and check in online with their Vinyl Nation friends in other cities. Wireless throughout for their laptops. I could see adding a bunch of computers dedicated to online poker and online bridge."

"Now you're talking," Theo grinned.

"Or maybe tables for face-to-face bridge and poker. Whatever the community wants."

"And is willing to pay for. It just might work. Might need a new name though. You plan to do all this over the next two years?"

"Sure. Think I've forgotten about Findependence Day? This is my dream."

"No," Theo laughed. "Never for a moment did I imagine you had."

■ ■ ■

For a charity fundraiser in late April, Al fixed Jamie up with Jocelyn, the ambitious graduate they'd encountered at the last Consumer Electronics Show. Al knew Jamie was putting in long hours and hadn't snapped out of the funk he'd been in since Sheena threw him out. Al himself had parted ways recently with Betty—his third wife—so he invited Jocelyn's friend Karen as his own date. To further buoy Jamie's spirits, Al invited Theo, despite their fleeting acquaintance, and told him to bring Ariana. When Theo said Ariana was in Seattle with a daughter, expecting their third grandchild, Al insisted Theo join the party anyway.

The Crystal Club was the closest the city came to the glitz of Vegas. The lighting was low. The white linen tablecloths were crisp and spotless, adorned with fresh flowers and candles. Affluent singles usually gathered here to dance to an incessant beat of techno-pop and hip-hop. Tonight, though, a versatile jazz orchestra catered to a more sedate crowd. The over-priced dinner and show headliner would be followed by the usual corporate hoopla.

Al had asked everyone to arrive by eight-thirty, but when they sat down in their booth and ordered their drinks, Jamie still hadn't shown up. Jocelyn drained her cocktail at a single swig, then leaned forward to adjust a strap on her shoe. Al couldn't help but appreciate her more obvious gifts, made all the more noticeable by the sliver slip of fabric that passed as a dress. How they could charge so much for so little fabric was beyond him.

The first notes of "In the Mood" drifted over the table, as the band shifted from light classical to swing.

"Jamie tells me the public offer's almost in the bag," Theo said, raising his voice over the music.

"It's dragging on," Al said. "Always one more document the guys in Finance need to see. If I'd known how complicated it was, I might have stayed private."

"But then you'd never make the big score. I have at least two clients who went public. That's where the big money is."

"I assume you yourself have already reached financial independence?" Al addressed the older man.

Dressed in a tailor-made navy suit and silk shirt, Theo exuded the confidence of age and wealth. "I practice what I preach. I never made the monster score like some of my clients but then we have relatively simple needs."

Al took this as a confession the guy wasn't a big-time operator. All the losers he knew had "simple needs." He kept his face impassive.

"So you're still working?"

Theo nodded. "I enjoy my work and clients, like our young friend, if he ever arrives." He glanced at his watch, "I'm fascinated by financial markets."

"You must be a great stock-picker. Be sure to pick up some Far East Electronica the day it comes out."

"I'm not a big fan of picking individual growth stocks," Theo said, "particularly not IPOs."

"Mutual funds then?"

"We own a few for certain mandates: small-caps, precious metals, deep global value. But the core of my client portfolios are in low-cost exchange-traded funds and a few dividend-paying blue chip stocks."

"ETFs."

"Right. You use those too?"

"Nah," Al scoffed. "I'm a stock-picker. I don't believe in financial advisors. I do my trading directly, online." He nodded at the waiter. "We have one more guest who hasn't arrived," he said, "but we'll order starters."

Theo must have been mulling over Al's dig at financial advisors. As soon as the waiter left he said. "Do you really think Jamie would have come this far without an advisor?"

"Probably not. Young people with no direction can be helped by a financial planner. But those commissions. The wealthier they get, the more you make. Makes me wonder whose retirement you really care about, your own or your clients."

A spasm of irritation crossed Theo's face. "You're talking about advisors who charge a fee based on client assets under management."

"Right." Al peered down his nose. "The way I figure it, 1% of $1 million is $10,000. Way too much."

"When I was an asset-based advisor my fee would taper down past that level. Most clients seemed to think I added enough value to justify the fee, especially if a portion of it was tax-deductible. Naturally I agree."

"What, for picking a bunch of ETFs?"

"That's one aspect. I agree you could do that part yourself through a discount broker, if you had the time and interest."

Theo paused to sip his drink. Karen and Jocelyn had finished their conversation. There was an awkward silence at the table. "The real value we bring comes from the tax side," Theo said, "the financial planning, estate planning, insurance and perhaps most of all the behavioural side."

"I don't follow," Al winked at Karen, who had begun to listen to the conversation. Karen had dressed more casually than Jocelyn, which left Al feeling vaguely irritated. It's an expensive sweater, he thought, but this is a $500-a-plate dinner. Couldn't she make a little effort?

"Hand-holding when the markets get rough," Theo said. "Left to their own devices, clients do the wrong thing at the wrong time. They buy when the sun is shining but once the clouds roll in, they don't know how to sell or rebalance."

"Rebalance?" Karen bravely interjected. The way she was looking at Theo only increased Al's irritation.

"Rejig the mix of stocks, bonds and other asset classes," Theo said to Karen. "For example, if at the end of the year you have a big gain in U.S. large caps, you might want to take partial profits in the U.S. and add to your position in Emerging Markets if they're depressed. Or if bonds had a great year, take some profits and add to equities while the market is selling at bargain prices."

"Doesn't sound so hard," Karen said with an admiring look.

"Not in theory," Theo said, "but most clients sit on their hands when the market is down. They only get back in once the market has come off its lows, so they miss the real bargains."

Al nodded, unconvinced.

"The other point," Theo said to Al, "is that I'm no longer an asset-based advisor. I charge by the hour or by the project."

"So I could pay you for a financial plan?" Karen said.

"Sure, for a one-time plan you could."

"Haven't I seen you before?" Karen said to Theo.

"Maybe on TV. Once in a while I fly down to Chicago to appear on Didi Quinlan's *Debt March*."

"That's where I saw you. I love that show. I can really relate to her guests."

"You have lots of debt?"

"Tons. I love shopping."

"Then forget this conversation about investing. Do what Didi says and focus on paying off your debts before you start thinking about how to invest."

"But guerrilla frugality sounds so boring," she said.

At that moment, Jamie arrived, making his apologies. "Traffic was unbelievable," he said. "Remind me to take a cab next year."

Al introduced him to Jocelyn and Karen. Jamie smiled warmly. "You were both at the show last year." He sat down in the booth next to Jocelyn, trying not to crowd her.

"You remember Jamie," Al said in an aside to Jocelyn.

"He was cute," Jocelyn whispered. "But married. And acted like he was."

"He won't be much longer," Al said. Then, in his normal voice, he gestured in Theo's direction. "And thanks to this gentleman, he's on the verge of becoming financially independent."

"Thanks should go to you," Theo said, raising his glass for a toast. "Here's to Jamie's employer." Glasses clinked all 'round.

"We were talking about guerrilla frugality," Theo said. "I was about to tell Karen that you and Sheena were just like her 20 years ago."

"Were we ever," Jamie grinned. "Worse."

"Jamie and I met on that show," Theo said.

"You're kidding! So you're both celebrities."

Karen leaned forward, her interest piqued in Jamie. For the first time, Al felt the ten-year gulf between his and Jamie's ages as the younger man drew the girls' attention.

"Say," Karen said. "Aren't you the classic rock critic? I love that old music."

"That's me," grinned Jamie. "You know the Vinyl Nation web site?"

"Heard of it. Isn't that where boomer geezers hang out?"

Al laughed now that Jamie shared his discomfort over their age differences.

"I'm not a boomer myself," Jamie protested. "I just own the site. Now my friend Theo on the other hand …"

Theo took Jamie's friendly ribbing with good grace.

Jocelyn reached over and ran her fingers lightly through Jamie's curly hair. "Yuck! What's this, a grey hair?"

Jamie pleaded guilty. *At least I have hair!*

"You're old enough to be my dad."

"Maybe not quite," Al said, "but the rest of us are. Jamie has two kids about to head off to college."

"Which reminds me," Jamie addressed Theo. "Now another year has passed, didn't you say I had to do something about the twins' education plans?"

"Right. Once college is less than five years away, you start reducing stock market risk by building up a ladder of strip bonds."

"We did that last year. We sold 25% of the equity funds to buy a strip bond maturing in August of the year they go to university."

"And the previous two years we did the same. So by now you have strip bonds maturing at the end of the first three summers they'll be in college. Now it's time to sell another 25% and take care of year four."

"Enough money talk," Al said, lifting his hand to signal the waiter. "Time for another round." The two women decided it was time to check their lipstick and headed giggling to the ladies room.

Nudging Jamie, Al glanced after their dates and said in his best contrived Cockney accent, "That Jocelyn's a bit of all right."

"Karen's cuter and she seems more impressed with my web site."

"She's my date. Forget it." Al tried to sound light-hearted.

"Hey," Jamie added as the drinks arrived, "I thought you were trying to help me get over a broken heart."

"It doesn't look that broken. Why don't you ask Jocelyn out next week? We can make it a double date."

"I don't know. She thinks I'm a geezer."

Al sipped from a tall crystal tulip glass.

"Hate to break it to you but in their eyes, you *are* an old geezer. But they don't mind. They know geezers have all the money, don't they, Theo?"

"To tell you the truth, Al," Jamie said, "I'm seriously trying to patch things up with Sheena." His sincerity was all too apparent to Al.

"What are you, nuts? You've got a world of sweet young things to conquer. Plenty more where they come from."

"Call me crazy. I'm like Woody Allen's pigeons. I believe in mating for life, even if Sheena seems determined to go it alone."

Al looked at him in mock disgust. "You *are* nuts," he said.

Chapter 15

May Be a Price to Pay

[ALAN PARSONS PROJECT, 1984]

T he next week, early in May, Al and his Far East Electronica executive team, including Jamie, had to meet again with the accountants. To avoid drawing attention to the cramped headquarters in the industrial park, Al had booked a meeting room in an elegant marble and glass hotel in the city centre.

FEE had been sending reams of documents to the accounting firm, and the bean counters had been locked up with the company's finance guys for weeks. It was very close to IPO time. Al could almost count the money.

He wore his best dark blue suit to the meeting, with a crisp white dress shirt and—in a departure from his customary open-necked collar and gold chain—a conservative tie. He'd also bought a pair of black Gucci loafers. He'd long believed more business deals were lost over nondescript shoes than any other detail.

Al had been pushing the board to let him roll the presses on the new annual report. He'd hired an ad agency to transform its normally dry prose into a glossy marketing vehicle, something appropriate for a new public offering Al likened to "the next Microsoft or Google."

The problem was the accountants. They weren't signing off on the dull stuff at the back. Every time Al approved a set of galley proofs for the report, it came back with footnotes circled and questioned. Finally, he agreed to meet with the accountants to sort it out. They came from a mid-sized accounting firm he'd switched to a year earlier.

When the meeting began, the first partner to speak was Jack Rexfield, 32 years old, blonde and athletic. He looked more like a professional ball player than an accountant. Al found it hard to believe he would choose such a dull profession.

Today, Rexfield looked the part. He wasn't smiling, and slight frown lines creased his forehead. "I'm afraid the news is not good, gentlemen," he began. "There appear to be some irregularities that we've been unable to reconcile."

Al sat stone-faced, trying not to show any emotion at this revelation. The rest of the room remained quiet.

Rexfield switched on his laptop, slipped in a flash drive and called up the first of several PowerPoint slides. "We've identified two consecutive quarters when revenues appear to have been inflated, with management bonuses calculated according to those inflated values."

"This," he called up the next slide, "shows invoices issued totalling $1.7 million in Q4 of last year and $1.1 million in Q1 this year, which are only now going to be written down against bad debt. These invoices were apparently issued to non-existent clients and were used solely to inflate revenues for the purpose of boosting management bonuses."

He flipped through a few more slides, but Al had the general idea. He'd chosen Rexfield in the hope he was too inexperienced to notice the shell game he'd engineered. Apparently, Rexfield was sharper than he'd thought.

Rexfield reached for a file and addressed his colleagues and the FEE team directly. "I'm sorry to be the bearer of such news," he said, "but in light of such irregularities, we won't be able to sign off on the books this year. It's my opinion the public offering should not proceed. I believe there must be a full internal audit before any further capital is raised."

Al remained quiet, but Jamie asked a question.

"How about the debt side? Will the bank extend our line of credit?"

Rexfield considered this for a second and focused on the back of the room. *He's avoiding eye contact with me*, Al thought.

"If I were the bank, I would not do so," Rexfield said finally.

Jamie wasn't satisfied and pressed on. "Can we raise more capital privately?" Jamie asked.

Sit down, you fool. You're only going to make it worse.

"That's not clear either," Rexfield said. "It appears our angel investors have offset their risk by committing a chunk of their equity position to three large Japanese investors. The shareholder agreement permits that, as long as they have the votes to pass it. But there was also a huge warrant kicker slipped through the board to let the new guys take control for relatively little investment. From what I can tell, effective control of Far East Electronica has passed to a holding company owned by those investors. They will have the final say on a public offering or any other major corporate move."

Now a babble of angry voices and questions rose from the executives around the table. They'd sat in stunned silence until Jamie started to ask questions. Clenched fists were raised, while accusations flew back and forth across the boardroom table.

In the midst of the confusion, Al saw his chance to slip away. Jamie was quick to follow and buttonholed Al in the adjoining corridor.

"What was that all about?"

"Who knows? Punk kid doesn't know squat about accounting."

"He went to a top-notch business school," Jamie said. "He's a chartered accountant and a chartered financial analyst. It's pretty clear he knows his stuff." Jamie placed his hand on Al's arm. "What's going on, Al?"

"Don't worry about it," Al said, shrugging off Jamie's hand. "It will all blow over."

Jamie's eyes narrowed with suspicion.

"Are they pointing the finger at you? Rexfield didn't say that."

"He didn't have to."

"Is there something you haven't told me?" Jamie gave Al a look of uneasy puzzlement. Al could hear the boardroom door open and slam, and he heard more angry voices.

"We can't talk here," he said. "Follow me."

They half ran down the corridor, through the hotel lobby and out the exit. Outside, with a doorman just ten yards away, Al lit a cigarette and offered one to Jamie.

"You started smoking again?" Jamie said, shaking his head as he declined.

"Just this once." Al gazed out at the street, watching the taxis searching for fares.

Jamie cleared his throat. "What do I need to know about what just happened in that boardroom?"

"What would you like to know?" Al's eyes widened innocently.

"For starters, what was all that about ownership of FEE passing to a Japanese conglomerate?"

Al walked a few feet to put some distance between them and the doorman.

"It may be true."

"May be true? What are you saying?"

"I'm saying I had to sell pieces of equity to keep this ship afloat. I piggybacked on the Japanese deal with the angels to pay a few bills for the company and to maintain my modest lifestyle."

"What equity? How much? You couldn't do that without authorization. Have you diluted my founders' shares?"

"Read the shareholders' agreement. I told you over and over that if you wanted a major piece of the action you had to buy in. If you'd put up that $50,000 when I asked you, you'd have more than quintupled your money."

"That was for a later-stage financing," Jamie stared at Al with fascinated horror. "How much are my founders' shares worth now?"

Al looked away, took a long drag of his cigarette. This ain't going to be easy, he thought. *Poor kid.*

"What founders' shares?"

"Those thousand shares you said you'd put aside at the very beginning. I never could pin you down on what percentage it was."

"Did you get that in writing?"

"Well, no. We were friends, dammit. I figured you'd take care of it. I trusted you."

Al stubbed his cigarette into the ground. "As our mutual buddy Eric Burdon once sang with the Animals, 'I'm just a boy whose intentions are good ...'"

■ ■ ■

It was one of those flawless spring days that usually made Jamie's spirits soar. That was hardly the case this Saturday morning, as he awoke in the walk-up apartment he'd occupied for over four months.

The modern furniture couldn't relieve the gloom of the place, but he didn't plan to stay long enough to give the apartment even a new coat of paint, let alone renovate it. The constant noise from Lakefront Boulevard was starting to wear him down. He missed Sheena and the twins.

If I were at home, I'd be in the garden with them right now, planting dahlias or nagging Marco to mow the lawn. Instead I'm cooped up in this dive.

He put the teakettle on and again replayed the events of the board meeting that had ended his week. The more he thought about it, the more he was incensed by Al's betrayal. The personal betrayal didn't bother him so much, but the betrayal of all the shareholders and management team did. They'd sweated blood for the company.

Delaying FEE's initial public offering was one thing, but it wasn't at all clear to Jamie that FEE even had a future now, public or private.

Had the public offering proceeded on schedule by the summer, it would soon have emerged that he'd been cheated out of his founder shares. The injustice of it gnawed at him. Be an owner, not a loaner. He'd taken that advice to heart and helped build an enterprise, only to have it torn from his grasp.

His initial reaction to Al's shell game was to feel not just emotional pain, but actual physical pain, as well. Like the time he'd been blindsided after a whistle in a hockey game. His first reaction wasn't anger at the player who'd delivered the blow. It was physical pain and the urgent imperative to get his wind back. Anger came later.

Jamie had often performed rough calculations of the value of his small stake in FEE on the open market. Coupled with the rest of his financial plan, he'd hoped it would put him over the top for Findependence Day. Now he'd have to scrap that idea and with it the employment income he had been counting on for one more year.

Jamie walked to the window and raised it to let in the fresh spring air. He breathed deeply and smelled the delicious aroma of a nearby bakery. The clakkety clack of the streetcars was loud but his mind was racing too much to notice.

There would be one or two more paycheques from FEE, possibly more if he refused to resign and came in often enough to witness the end game. After that, there would be some severance and ultimately a bit of income from Employment Insurance. It gave him an eerie sense of déjà vu nine years after he'd been ejected from Tech Heaven.

But Jamie's financial resources were more substantial now. He hoped he wouldn't have to draw down on his Tax-Free Savings Account, but it was comforting to know the money was there if he needed it.

The end of FEE and the draining of the pot of gold that he'd anticipated at the end of that rainbow did not mean the end of Findependence Day, merely a postponement.

Perhaps he'd have to move it back two or three years, but one thing he knew: He'd never again kowtow to the Jharhids and Als of the world. Employment had always provided his surest stream of income, but Jamie realized he'd finally outgrown it.

The whole point of Findependence Day was to be free to do what you really wanted to do. Jamie realized he already had enough baseline income from other sources to pursue his passion now, not a few years from now. When he first put together the plan with the help of Bernie and Theo, that passion was to write songs and compose electronic music and one day perhaps perform it on the road.

His passion still involved music, but he now realized he wasn't by nature a composer. He glanced at the electronic keyboard in the corner of his living room, silently admonishing him for letting it sit unused. He didn't bound out of bed each morning to pound the keyboards. He was a music fan, more apt to slip a piece of black vinyl on to a turntable and crank up the volume. Then he would sign on to his web site and chat with his cyber friends around the world.

Or he'd dash off a blog entry that drew parallels between the insights of half-forgotten musicians, whose poetic inspirations were as relevant to the 21st century as the one in which they were composed.

Jamie thought of the American folksinger Phil Ochs, who'd hanged himself in despair over the disparity between his artistic vision and the reality of day-to-day America. From *Pleasures of the Harbour* to *Rehearsals for Retirement*, Ochs had charted a unique course. Jamie's blog tried to do justice to such artists and to help new generations rediscover them. In the meantime, the Vinyl Nation community endeavoured to preserve the very medium on which this rich musical legacy resided.

He walked over to his turntable and started listening to the last album he'd placed on it. Theo had turned him on to Mahler. Jamie flung himself on the couch, closed his eyes and tried to focus on listening to his fifth symphony. But his thoughts wouldn't stop.

He realized financial independence did not exist in a vacuum but was intimately tied up with artistic and spiritual independence. At one level, it was little more than the stubborn child's insistent declaration that "I'm the boss of me." At another, he realized any kind of independence is a fragile entity.

He recalled from his youth the gnarled old cook in his parents' restaurant who told him, enigmatically and ungrammatically, "It don't pay to be independent." Until now, he'd never been quite sure what the old guy had meant.

Perhaps he was saying we are all members of communities and are therefore interdependent. The founding chairman of the most successful corporation still has bosses: shareholders, customers, regulators, the courts. No man is an island.

Theo had told him all this, sometimes gently or indirectly, and Jamie had listened. Over the years he had changed his original vision of Findependence Day, just as the actual date itself had moved forward and backward as circumstances changed. To be sure, "July 4th, on my 50th birthday" had become his north star, forever pointing the way when his secondary goals faltered. In his heart, he knew outrageous circumstance might force a revision of the goal to, perhaps, "July 4th, on my 56th birthday" but the power of the goal still propelled him well along the path.

He'd encountered many a sceptic along the way. "Who wants to retire at 50?" one would say. "What are you going to do all day long? Play bingo?" Or, "after six months of golf and poker, you'll be pounding on your employer's door to return." Or, "Most jobs are marginally better than daytime television."[12]

Jamie would try to explain that, in theory, how he spent any given day would be totally at his discretion the day after Findependence Day. Each hour would be his to dispose of as he saw fit. But, in practice, he'd add, those days would be very much like all that had preceded it. He'd wake up at much the same time in the morning—possibly earlier—and go about the routines of life, much the same as he ever had. The human body and soul do not, after all, change so very much merely because the economic system that houses them has changed in some abstract way. The body still must be clothed, fed and exercised. The soul must soldier on regardless, seeking human companionship, artistic, cultural and ultimately spiritual inspiration.

His critics were right and they were also wrong. Findependence Day changed nothing but changed everything. For most people, he knew, most of life would precede Findependence Day. When Bismarck conceived the first pension, few people lived to the age at which it became available. But in the modern world, those who charted their financial lives in advance and persevered stood a chance of enjoying 30 or 40 years of what was once called "retirement."

Findependence Day was never about doing nothing. Jamie realized that, while not precisely a mirage, financial independence would see him doing exactly what he'd been doing all these years. Not selling electronic gadgets for Tech Heaven, to be sure. And not travelling the world as a hired mercenary for the Als of the world.

Vinyl Nation was another story. The day after he turned 50, he wasn't about to stop blogging. He wasn't going to stop listening to contemporary or classic popular music or even the classical masterpieces of centuries past. All that would continue. He would also continue to chat on his site with his friends and, were he to achieve his vision of an Internet Cafe, he would talk to many of them in the flesh.

Al had kicked him where it hurt. But now Jamie could see clearly what he had to do. His avocation would become his vocation, not eventually but now. His hobby site would become his sustenance during the years he'd told Sheena were the "best yet to come."

Those years were supposed to have been shared with Sheena. The thought of his feisty, redheaded soul mate interrupted his Findependence Day reverie.

No way I'm giving up on that woman, he thought. There can't be any 'best is yet to come' without Sheena. *I need to win her back and start living my best years.*

■ ■ ■

The grand opening of *Platters*—the new name for Jamie's Internet Café—was scheduled the week before Labour Day. Shocked as he'd been by Sheena's insistence on selling 38 Verdant Crescent, Jamie admitted grudgingly to himself it was the

[12]First attributed to Canadian computer consultant Art Benjamin.

best thing that could have happened. The proceeds from the sale were split down the line, providing the working capital Jamie needed to proceed with his plan.

Over the summer, Jamie and Bernie finalized the deal. They agreed that, over the next five years, Jamie would gradually buy both the business and the building, funding Bernie's own retirement. All those years of smoking—both cigarettes and other substances—had finally taken their toll on his health, and he was finally ready to move beyond semi-retirement to the full deal.

Jamie knocked down the walls between the Vinyl Cave and the low-end coffee shop next door. Sheena was right about real estate, he thought. He also renovated the main floor and the basement.

The twins, about to enter the last year of high school, had both pitched in to plan the launch. They were enthusiastic about the concept for the whole café. It would be a replica of a '50s diner, complete with booths and jukebox. Each booth had white vinyl cushions and access to a traditional functioning music box to select classic 45s. In front of the counter was a row of single circular seats with chrome and red vinyl. Jamie's mum was only too happy to supply ideas and recipes for the burgers and shakes that went with the '50s theme.

Not least, Michaela made the convincing case to name the café *Platters*. "The records and the food, Dad," she said. "Platters. Get it?"

The colour scheme was black and white, with plenty of chrome. On the walls were classic art covers of the vinyl LP era, but unlike Bernie's more pedestrian approach of stapling them to the walls of his store, Jamie had them properly framed. He filled in the bare spots with some old 45s.

At the opening, Jamie hardly recognized Marcello in his elegant rented tux. Marcello had volunteered to be the evening's deejay between sets of a live band. He'd been practising spinning platters for weeks in anticipation of his debut.

Michaela, elegant in a black-and-white dress, waved to her dad as she rolled by on old-time roller skates, serving hors d'oeuvres. She was assisted by Jocelyn and Karen, who were also in skates, though more self-conscious about it.

Michaela had come up with the idea of using old 45s as an invitation. She mailed out records to Bernie's customers and to everyone on the contact lists of the entire family. Meanwhile word went out at the Vinyl Nation web site that all were invited. Anyone who brought a 45 or long-playing record would be admitted, no questions asked.

The buzz was that a band that had first met through the site would be playing. Sure enough, *The Geezers* came through, performing covers of classics from the '60s and '70s but sprinkling in a few of their own compositions. When they got to a Sha Na Na medley, they invited Jamie to take a mike and share the lead vocals. He strapped on a guitar and pretended to strum as he belted out a fair version of "Rock and Roll Is Here to Stay."

It was a high, but Jamie felt a pang. If only Sheena were here, he thought wistfully, it would be perfect. *It wasn't right that she was missing his big night.* He fervently hoped someone had caught the moment on video.

He relinquished his spot in the limelight at the end of the first set. By the time the second set began, the place was rocking. That's when Theo and Ariana arrived.

"Great party," Theo remarked, brandishing an old 45 of Petula Clark's "Downtown." Ariana and Jamie exchanged hugs.

"Couldn't have done it without the kids," Jamie glanced with pride at the teens rolling by with their trays of hors d'oeuvres. He grabbed a mini-burger. When the café opened the next day, the '50s menu would feature full-sized gourmet burgers, shakes, sodas and other comfort food.

Jamie placed the 45 on a growing pile of vinyl in the center of the café. Four couples danced around the periphery.

Every seat was occupied. The noisy babble of introductions competed with the music. "So you're Old Hand," one cyber identity told another as they met in the flesh for the first time, "I always thought you were older." Or "Plastic Gal. I never guessed you were actually a man!"

Overhearing the last exchange, Theo said, "I have a confession to make. I'm Greek Tycoon."

"You're kidding," Jamie's eyes widened with surprise. "You were always Advisor Guy. Everyone knew that."

"There was no prohibition against having multiple identities," Theo explained. "Back in the early days before the site achieved critical mass, I created Greek Tycoon just to make it look like you had more regular posters. Sometimes he'd argue with Advisor Guy. I guess you could say I was arguing with myself, which often happens with us financial advisors."

"I should have guessed. It's so obvious."

"I thought you knew. That's why I chose a handle I figured you'd twig to."

Jamie made a mock "shoot me" motion with his finger pointed at his head. Then he grabbed Ariana's hand and beckoned Theo to join them. "I want to show you something."

They walked down the stairs to the basement, which was decked out with chairs and traditional card tables. No one was playing, but several couples sat at the tables, engaged in animated conversations about the goings-on at the web site. Jamie indicated a shelf that contained dozens of packs of playing cards, poker chips, bridge bidding boxes and other paraphernalia.

"Poker or bridge, take your pick," he said. "Sunday through Wednesday nights, we're running duplicate bridge. The rest of the week is devoted to poker. We've also book marked the major online bridge and poker sites on the terminals upstairs."

"I'll take bridge, thank you very much," Theo said. Then, pensively, "Do you remember the first time we talked here?"

"I do indeed. It was 20 years ago today," he sang, and Theo completed the lyric, "Sergeant Pepper told the band to play."

"Well, not quite to the day."

"You should be proud," Theo said. "This appears to be the perfect small business for your post-Findependence Day years."

"This is just the beginning," Jamie's voice was animated. He outlined his plans to franchise the concept throughout North America. "Why stop here?"

Theo frowned, in the midst of walking back up to the main floor of the café. "Jamie, a one-off local business is one thing, and it's a fun little operation. But if you're starting to talk franchises, you're biting off more than you can chew."

"Why not? My credit is good. I know how to raise capital."

"You went down that road with Far East Electronica. Look how that ended." Jamie tried not to let his face betray his disappointment.

"This is different," Jamie insisted.

"I don't think so. Franchising is a tough row to hoe. Be content with one location and leave it at that. Don't forget, this is your Findependence Day fun."

"He's right," a familiar voice suddenly intruded from behind the computer banks. "Who cares about vinyl?"

It took a few seconds for Jamie to put a face to the voice.

By that time, Al was in front of him, shaking Theo's hand. "Hello old friend," Al said, as if nothing had ever happened. "Last I saw you was that charity ball."

Theo shrugged but didn't reply.

"What are you doing here?" Jamie said at last.

Al waved an old 45 in front of him. " 'Kind of a Hush' by Herman's Hermits. Never did like it much."

"I didn't know you were a Vinylhead."

"I sometimes lurk," Al said. "Besides, Karen and Jocelyn told me they had a gig for the launch. Wouldn't want to miss it." His face scrunched up in mock pain. "I'm miffed you didn't extend a personal invitation."

"Miffed doesn't begin to describe how I feel about what you did to Far East Electronica," Jamie said.

"That was just business," Al shrugged. He shrugged off all negativity as if it were a minor nuisance. "Things happen. Listen to your friend Theo and keep this operation small. You don't need the hassle I had to endure."

Jamie looked at Theo but said nothing. Al sipped his drink. "Strange crowd," he said. "About what you'd expect from an Internet community. All shapes and sizes. But I'd be surprised if you could wrench any cash out of them. No real business here. Certainly not franchisable. Mark my words, the '50s are passé and vinyl is dead."

He began to leave, then turned and tossed the 45 gently, like a Frisbee.

It landed at Jamie's feet.

Chapter 16

Time Is on My Side

[ROLLING STONES, 1964]

B usiness boomed during the first month of operation of *Platters*. The launch party fuelled enthusiastic word of mouth, and positive local media coverage drove many new patrons through the doors of the fledgling enterprise. Jamie worked non-stop, seven days a week. By October, he was ready for a breather. When Theo invited him to bring Jocelyn up north to help close his cottage over the long weekend, he accepted gladly.

The three-hour trip on the Friday of the long weekend was therapeutic in itself. After long days in the café, the fall colors soothed Jamie's soul. He and Jocelyn took turns driving so they both could enjoy the scenery.

Theo and Ariana seemed glad to see them. After they unpacked, they joined their hosts for cocktails in the comfortable log cabin, then sat down for dinner in an enclosed veranda. A few stars punched through a light cloud cover. Jamie felt the calm of their surroundings creep into his tired body and smiled across the flickering candles at his young companion.

Over medium-rare lamb and spring salad, Ariana and Jocelyn chatted about the latter's growing freelance business in event management.

"Let me tell you from bitter experience," Jamie told Jocelyn, "You don't want to go back to being employed by a corporation. Be your own boss. Build a business that you can one day sell."

"I'm trying," Jocelyn said, munching on a sweet carrot stick. "But the economy isn't exactly on a roll."

"That's why I think the time is right to expand *Platters*," Jamie said, refilling all four glasses.

"Could work," Jocelyn said. "Think big."

"Theo doesn't think franchising is the way to go but it worked for Tim Horton's coffee empire."

"I'd have a serious rethink on that," Theo said. "Few businesses are candidates for franchising. I've had several clients get involved with various aspects of franchising, and it's no easy road."

"Terrific," Jamie said, still enthusiastic. "You can be my franchising consultant."

"I don't think so," Theo said, his face taut.

"What about taking the web site to the next level?" Jamie persisted. "Traffic's way up since the launch. Three more advertisers signed up for banner ads."

"Who?"

"Grey Insurance and two banks. They're targeting the over-50 crowd."

"Good," Theo said. "Be happy with a nice little auxiliary stream of small-business income and leave it at that. And I'd seriously consider a name change."

"Like what? The twins have been nattering at me about that too. When their friends come over, they always avoid using the word 'vinyl'."

Theo looked thoughtful. "They may have a point."

Jamie mimicked Michaela's voice: "Like dad, vinyl is so embarrassing."

"Does she have a better suggestion?"

"Sure. They think it should be called FindependenceDay.com."

Theo laughed. "Well, duh," he said, mimicking the teen tone of voice. "Why didn't we think of that? Speaking of which, are you still committed to your own Findependence Day?"

"It's still circled on next year's calendar but it doesn't really matter. After Al cooked the books at Far East Electronica, I pretty much resigned myself to five more years of keeping my nose to the grindstone. But I've lucked out, because now I'm doing what I enjoy. It doesn't even seem like work."

"I never liked that man."

"I can't believe I was such a bad judge of character," Jamie said. "Al doesn't seem to realize he's a sleaze. He doesn't get it. He probably thinks he did me a favour by coming to the launch party."

Theo nodded, but didn't pursue the topic. He sipped his wine and changed the subject. "How's the Lazy ETF Portfolio bearing up?"

"Doing what it was designed to do. I've stopped watching the market's twists and turns. I take the media's coverage of short-term dips with a grain of salt."

"Good," Theo said, nodding in approval.

The moment he mentioned the word portfolio, Ariana and Jocelyn rolled their eyes in exaggerated frustration and moved into the living room to continue their conversation. From hints Ariana had dropped, Jamie knew she still considered Sheena as a close friend. Clearly, Ariana was not yet comfortable with the younger woman as the other half of a "Jamie and" couple. Still, the two women chatted amicably about a movie they'd both gone to recently.

Jamie looked at Theo and said, "I have a friend in the business who only looks at his brokerage statements once a year, and then only for rebalancing."

"I look more often than that but not every day or even every week." Theo looked outside. "The clouds have moved off. Let's get some fresh air and do some stargazing till Ariana brings out dessert. I'd bring your jacket."

Jamie refilled his wine goblet and joined Theo outside. There was the faintest hint of a chill in the air. "I'm not sure the women are interested in our chats about investing," Theo whispered. It was eerily quiet. Apart from the sporadic laughter coming from the cabin, the only sound was the gentle rustling of the evergreens when the wind came up.

Jamie zipped his jacket up half way and took in the starlit panorama. He was reflecting on his own cosmic insignificance when Theo broke the silence.

"I know you're upset that I don't think you should expand the Internet café. If the income it's generating dried up tomorrow, what shape would you be in?"

"I'm not sure. If I took 10% a year from my investments, I think I'd be doing fine."

"Unfortunately, with a 45-year time horizon, I don't think you should count on that much. After all, we have to assume you'll live to 95."

"How much, then?" Jamie zipped his jacket all the way to his neck.

"Less than half. Have you heard of an American financial planner named Bill Bengen?"

"No."

"He's written a book[13] on how long investment portfolios can last in retirement. His term for a safe annual withdrawal amount is SAFEMAX."

"How much does he think I can safely withdraw?"

"With a balanced portfolio of stocks and bonds, he reckons a little more than 4% a year in the first year, after which the annual withdrawal amount would be indexed to inflation."

"So if I have $500,000 I could withdraw $20,000 a year indefinitely without worrying about drawing down on capital?"

"Right."

"My father always had a rule. He insisted he and mum could never break into capital. He died too soon to enjoy any of it, but mum was glad he took that approach."

"That's one way to do it. Of course, if you didn't have any heirs you could handle it differently and die broke in your '90s."

"That's what my mum argued," said Jamie, "even though she had children. 'The heck with the kids,' she'd tell dad. 'I'm not dying with a million dollars in the bank for them to squander. The last cheque I'm writing will be to the undertaker, and it will bounce.'"

Theo laughed. In an excited tone, he said, "Did you see that?"

"What?"

Theo pointed to the northeast part of the sky. "A shooting star. It went clear across half the horizon to that tall tree over there."

"Didn't see it. I was still feeling sorry for the undertaker my mum plans to stiff."

Theo laughed and stared up at the stars, as if he were willing a second shooting star to appear. "Our lives are so fleeting, like that shooting star. That's why it's important to consider what kind of legacy you'll leave once you exit this stage."

Jamie scrunched his fists into his coat sleeves to warm his hands. "Sheena and I intend to leave the twins a substantial portion of our estate now that it's big enough

[13]See appendix, A Peek at Theo's Library

to worry about. What I can't figure is how much we need to salt away to ensure our own comfort in old age, and how much we need to set aside for Marcello and Michaela."

Theo paused to consider this.

"How much of a legacy you choose to leave your children is up to you," he said. "For some, it's money. For others, it's enough education to get them a start in life. Others expect enough for a first home or at least a down payment on one. I know some families that make sure the kids get enough to start their own business. There's no hard and fast rule."

"We're thinking maybe we'd leave half the estate for the twins. A quarter of the total for each. But what happens if we run through all our capital and we live past a hundred?"

"We?"

Jamie blushed. "I was thinking of Sheena. I keep forgetting."

Theo grinned, but tactfully avoided going down that road. "There's one other point about leaving a legacy. To some extent children are one's legacy, and the money you leave them is too. But the world's great philanthropists seek to leave a legacy not just for their immediate families but also for all mankind. Something worth considering."

"We're not here for a long time, that's for sure. It would be nice to remembered for something more than being the richest guy in the cemetery."

Theo nodded and glanced at the crescent moon, which had just emerged from behind a stray cloud. It was bright enough to light up his face. "Mind you, it may be a long time before you reach the cemetery. The advances we're seeing in medical science means your generation may live much longer than you ever dreamed."

Jamie looked at the moon. "That's good news. Of course it means our investments will have to last longer too."

Theo smiled. "You've heard the phrase longevity insurance?"

"Annuities?"

"Right. If you're really concerned about outliving your money, you can always convert some or all of your retirement savings to an annuity."

"From an insurance company?"

"Usually. They employ actuaries—those guys who did better than you at math in high school—who figure out how long you're likely to live. If you annuitize too early and die soon after, the insurance companies win. If you outfox them and live much longer than they ever dreamed, then you win."

"I like option B better," Jamie grinned.

"So do I. When you think about it, Sheena's Defined Benefit pension amounts to an annuity, as do Government pensions. In both cases, the recipient is assured of a guaranteed income for life, whether you live to be 60 or 600."

Jamie's face clouded. "But I don't have one of those gold-plated pension plans."

"No, but you could put some of your money into new variable annuity products that attempt to deliver much the same thing."

"Variable annuities?"

"Let's go back to the girls." Theo grabbed his arm, and they started walking back to the cottage.

"Earlier we were talking about fixed annuities," Theo said as they walked, "which behave more or less like fixed income. You give the insurance company a certain amount of capital and they undertake to provide a lifelong stream of income for you, generally more than you'd get if you invested in bonds."

"But with bonds, the capital is available later for, say, the twins. With fixed annuities, when I die, the capital dies with me, unless I pay extra for certain options to transfer payments to the surviving spouse."

Theo raised his eyebrows, seemingly impressed by how much Jamie had learned.

"Correct. That's like Sheena's employer pension or government pensions. When you die, the surviving spouse usually gets partial benefits, but on the second death the pension dies with you. The kids are out of luck. Annuities behave similarly."

"What about variable annuities?"

"They vary with the stock market and are big in the United States. If the market does well, you make more than you'd make with fixed annuities. If it doesn't, you at least get a certain minimum income."

"What about in this country?"

"Variable Annuities are also known as segregated funds and like their U.S. counterparts can come with guaranteed minimum withdrawal benefits. Some of the first-generation products guarantee a minimum annual withdrawal benefit only for a certain period, typically 14 to 20 years. Later improvements have extended that guarantee to life, making them another valid form of longevity insurance."

They'd reached the cottage, but Jamie had one more question. "I've heard some bad things about variable annuities," he said.

Before they stepped back onto the veranda, Theo said, "Variable annuities have their critics. There's a high cost to provide such guarantees. If you're really sharp you could reconstruct it yourself for a lower cost. In the end it's just one of several possible solutions you can throw into the retirement income mix."

They stepped onto the veranda just in time to see Ariana and Jocelyn placing yogurt and fruit on the table.

Jocelyn greeted Jamie with a warm smile. "Jamie, if you're still paying him by the hour, you can't afford any more advice."

Theo raised his hands. "Not to worry. I've disabled my meter."

"We missed you," Ariana said. "Did you show Jamie your new telescope?"

"Telescope?" cried Jocelyn. "It would be awesome to see the Milky Way through a telescope. What do you say, Jamie?"

"Sure."

"You're sure you wouldn't rather discuss variable annuities?" Theo said.

■ ■ ■

In January, Sheena decided to throw a party for the twins to celebrate their 18th birthday, and she agreed to invite their father. When Jamie arrived on the night of the party, he had to admit that Sheena had made a sound investment with her half of the proceeds from the sale of 38 Verdant Crescent.

Sheena had bought a reasonably priced tri-level townhouse. Located near the center of the city, it was closer to services and transit but still sufficiently distant from the clamor of downtown. The back deck overlooked the fourth hole of a public golf course. During golfing season, stray golf balls would find their way into the back yard.

Inside, the warm hardwood floors complemented the granite countertops in the kitchen. Sheena had hung a few new watercolors in the living room, all tastefully framed. In the open-concept living and dining area, Marco and Micki were putting the finishing touches on the "Happy 18th" metallic silver banner that they'd strung between the dining room and the main living area. Sheena was working at the kitchen island.

Almost as soon as he came inside, Michaela took her dad on a tour. Upstairs, she led him into two spacious bedrooms and an office on the middle floor. She simply pointed up the stairs to the private third-floor master suite.

Back on the main floor, Micki rejoined her brother. Jamie joined Sheena in the kitchen. She was wearing a sleek black and taupe tailored pantsuit and looked trimmer than he remembered. She'd reshaped her red bangs into a stylish short cut that accentuated her green eyes.

"You look great." Jamie chanced a kiss, planting his lips awkwardly between her left cheek and forehead. She didn't return the compliment.

"Heard about your launch." Sheena pushed him gently away as she reached for a spoon on the counter by the sink. "Too bad I couldn't make it. The twins told me all about the roller skates and the '50s diner theme."

"Credit your daughter for that one. Micki's marketing was brilliant. You should have come. The kids wanted you there. And I missed you." Jamie held her glance with his soft brown eyes.

The silence extended several heartbeats beyond polite conversation.

"I had a date."

Jamie felt like he'd been stabbed. He walked to the window and took in the view, as he regained his composure. With the leaves off the trees, the frozen river meandering through that part of the golf course was clearly visible from the townhouse. "Ever play this course?"

"Not in January."

"You guys send all your applications in to university?" he said, turning to the twins but addressing neither in particular.

"Sure, Dad," said Michaela. "Media studies at Western, computers at Waterloo."

"Big difference. Although I suppose the way the web is going, the two are pretty much converging."

The doorbell rang. Sheena excused herself to greet another early arrival.

"I heard a big web company was interested in your site," Marcello said.

"We have a nibble from Hooray!, the big social networking portal."

"Awesome. So Vinyl Nation could become part of Hooray?"

"Long shot. They think our demographics of wealthy baby boomers might be a good complement to their Gen X focus."

"We already told you, Dad," said Michaela. "The Vinyl Nation name sucks. Why don't you call it FindependenceDay.com?"

"Then Hooray would go for it for sure," said Marcello.

"I've already talked it over with Theo," said Jamie, "and it's a great idea. The problem is the original vinyl community doesn't want a name change."

"Why?"

"There's a sub-community who are threatening to split off if we sell to Hooray. Anyway, I don't think Hooray is all that interested."

Michaela shrugged.

Jamie tried again. "You study this stuff at school?"

"A bit," said Marcello.

"Maybe you could revamp the site for me? I'd pay you."

"I don't do HTML," said Michaela.

"Neither do I," said Marcello.

"You ever come on to the site?"

"Been there," said Michaela. "Not my scene."

"Me neither," said Marcello.

"Understandable. You're about three generations back of our focus."

"I do play vinyl though," said Michaela.

This was a surprise. "You're kidding."

"No, Dad," said Michaela, "Vinyl's making a comeback. Want to see my collection?"

"Sure, what have you got?"

"Standard geezer rock. Beatles. Stones. Airplane. Doors."

"I never imagined. What do you think, Marcello?"

"I just download like normal kids."

"So what universities are you applying to, Marco?"

"McGill. Penn State. Cornell."

"Woo, you want to study in the States?" Jamie said. "Not sure the old education plan is up to that one."

"I'm going to win a hockey scholarship at Cornell," Marcello said.

"Hockey? Thought soccer was your game."

"Depends on which sport will give me a scholarship."

"When you're not being a big jock on campus, what do you plan to study?"

"English and history."

"Like your mum. Going to become a teacher like her?"

"Maybe. Mum tells me they have a great pension."

Jamie grinned. Chips off the old block, he thought. *But he's the bond and she's the stock.*

Sheena returned with two guests in tow. She introduced them quickly to Jamie, but they were friends of Marco's; it took them about thirty seconds before they started talking to him and Michaela about other friends who were coming tonight.

When Sheena returned to the kitchen, Jamie said, "Hon, there's something I wanted to talk about."

Sheena gave him a frustrated look. "Not in front of the kids," she hissed. "The other guests will be here any minute."

"It won't take long. Let's go on the balcony."

Jamie slipped on his jacket and pushed open the sliding door, extending his hand to Sheena. This time she seemed less uncomfortable when he touched her. Sliding the door back into place, he said, "It's not what you're thinking."

"What am I thinking?" Her eyes were focused on the fourth hole, the red flag still waving in the breeze as a few snowflakes fluttered down.

"You miss me and are desperate to be reunited?" The sudden stillness in his eyes contrasted with his bantering tone, belying the depths of emotion he was really feeling. The cold wind reddened her cheeks, making her green eyes sparkle. She's still so beautiful, he thought. His heart ached.

She looked him in the eye. "Is that what you want? To get back together?"

"I don't know," Jamie stammered. "Yes, you know I do. I love you, and I always will. But that's not why I came here."

"You came here for your children's birthday."

"I did, but I also have a business proposition for you."

This seemed to surprise her.

"Business? With me? I have no interest in business."

"I thought perhaps you might take an interest, possibly with some of your buddies in the teachers' lounge."

"Does this have to do with selling out to Hooray? That's what I gathered from your chat with Michaela."

"Might. That's one aspect. But it's the other that may be more up your line."

Jamie told her about the deal with Bernie, including the fact he'd used his half of the house proceeds to put a hefty down payment on the whole building.

Sheena seemed wistful. "Real estate? I never could get you to spring for it."

"I know, and it was a big mistake on my part. Where do you think I've been living the last few years?"

"According to the twins, you're in some run-down apartment over *Platters*."

"For now. Like my parents, I'm living above the shop. The difference is I'm the landlord, not a tenant. I also lease out the third business unit to a dry cleaner."

She looked out again across the snow-swept course. A light gust of wind blew a few dead leaves across the green.

"Didn't you tell me there was also a coffee shop there?"

"There was," Jamie said excitedly. "But we let the lease expire and knocked down a wall between the two of them to create *Platters*."

"I'd like to see it some time."

"There just may be an opportunity to do that."

"What do you want from me?"

Sheena glanced pointedly inside to where the party was gathering. She wrapped her arms around her body against the chill.

"Putting aside the web site and Hooray!, I've been running the numbers with Bernie." He paused, trying to gauge her interest. "We figure a second location for *Platters* would double the cash flow but triple our profits. We'd like to test the concept in Rochester, perhaps with Victor. If we could interest a group of private investors, we could find out whether the concept can be duplicated in other locations. If so, it could be the beginning of something big. Franchising perhaps."

Sheena looked dubious and seemed anxious to get back to the party. "You're a dreamer. How much you trying to raise?"

"$100,000 per unit. I figure you teachers have so much bond income, some may be looking for a little action in private equity."

"I don't think so."

"You're always telling me how well set some of your teacher friends are. Especially the couples that are both in the profession."

"I want you to succeed, Jamie, I really do. And I hope you find the financing if you think a second store is the only way to go." Sheena had the grace to look uncomfortable, then added, "But I just can't ask my friends to do such a thing. Besides..."

"Yes?"

"All my friends have iPods."

Chapter 17

Takin' Care of Business

[BACHMAN-TURNER OVERDRIVE, 1973]

After the showdown in the FEE boardroom the previous year, Jamie had rebuffed every overture by Al Peters to patch up their differences. The two hadn't met since the *Platters* launch party, and hadn't exchanged much more than a few words on that occasion. Jamie knew Al had resurrected and restructured Far East Electronica. He certainly didn't expect Al to drop unannounced into the café, as he did late one morning in February. Jamie wasn't even there when Al arrived.

For about 15 minutes, Al poked around the record bins, selecting some great old vinyl titles from his youth: Black Sabbath, Deep Purple, Judas Priest. When he took them to the cashier at the front, the cute student manning the till placed the records in a red custom-made *Platters* bag. "So Wendy," Al said, "where's the boss today?" *Nice touch, having the kids' names stitched on their outfits.*

Wendy stopped chewing her gum. "He'll be here in a few minutes," she said, "for the lunch rush."

"I'll have a coffee and cheeseburger, medium rare. When Jamie comes out, can you tell him someone's waiting for him?"

"Sure thing."

Al took a seat at an unoccupied booth. Another ten minutes passed before Jamie walked in and scanned the busy room. Seeing Al, he stopped for a moment before walking slowly to his table.

"Been quite a while, guy," Al said when Jamie stopped at his table. "You seem to be out of the habit of returning my calls." Nervously, he fingered the gold chain he habitually wore underneath his open-necked black shirt.

Jamie didn't reply. Al fiddled with the lever on the jukebox music selector. "This thing work?"

Jamie nodded. Al inserted two quarters, chose a heavy-metal rock title, and the din soon reverberated across the café.

"Here's the thing," Al continued. "I know you're still upset about the shares. At the time, there wasn't much I could do about it. I was between a rock and a hard place."

"That and the shock of your fancy accounting and losing my job. Yeah, you might say I haven't been anxious to renew our acquaintance."

"Jamie," Al spread his hands. "It was business."

"I'm starting to understand the conflicting demands of running a business," Jamie said, almost sympathetically.

"We have some new private investors who injected new funds in FEE. I think I can make the case for making you whole. We've been friends a long time, and I want to do the right thing by you."

Jamie was silent, but he didn't walk away.

"I believe I've found a way I can convince my people to go along with it," Al said.

"How?"

"At the launch party, you mentioned something interesting about the need for a new product FEE could supply."

Jamie gave him a blank look.

"Remember you said it was a pity the Vinylheads didn't have an easy way to preserve the music?"

Now Jamie's interest was obvious. "Yes, I said it's easy to make CDs out of CDs and you can convert the music on vinyl to the CD format. And you can go from vinyl to tape."

Al took a sip from the coke Wendy had brought him.

"But there's no mass-market device available that will let you move from vinyl to vinyl," Jamie said. "Not at the retail level anyway."

"I got to thinking about that void in the marketplace," Al said. "If this vinyl renaissance is as enduring as you believe, we could get a supplier in Asia to develop a prototype vinyl-to-vinyl conversion unit."

"It would be expensive."

"Several thousand dollars but that shouldn't be insurmountable, if this niche market is as affluent as you say it is. They have the money and if they're true audiophiles they'd jump at the chance to buy such a device."

"It would help preserve the legacy," Jamie said, with growing animation. "My whole message was that the big manufacturers had vacated the field and there was no grassroots device available to keep the music from dying."

"To use the analogy of your monks in the middle ages, it would be the equivalent of giving them photocopy machines to preserve their written culture."

"You might be on to something there, Al."

Al knew from his voice that Jamie was excited.

"You're your own man now," Al said. "So if you want to consult to FEE on the development of the product, we could put you on retainer. We'd put through the share deal at the same time. I'm sure the new board would have no objections."

"Sounds reasonable," Jamie said, his eyes no longer suspicious. "I'd have to do more research on the concept. Think your suppliers are up to it?"

"I know for a fact one of them is. I've been making inquiries. Cost is a barrier. The first generation would be prohibitively expensive for all but the wealthiest Vinylheads."

"That's the way it's always been in our industry."

"Precisely. There's one other thing I'd like to propose."

Jamie's eyes narrowed. He hadn't come round completely.

"Yes?" Jamie said. Al could hear the suspicion in the word. *Not that I blame him.*

Al put another 50 cents in the machine. "Any tune you'd prefer?"

"Anything but heavy metal."

Al selected an Elton John tune he figured would be more to Jamie's liking. "I know you were upset at yourself for not participating in the second round of financing."

Jamie's face was impassive. "Not really. When you failed, I thanked the good lord I'd had the sense to pass."

"We went through a rough patch but let me assure you that you would have made a nice return had you done so."

"Well, I didn't."

"Here's what I propose. I've been watching the progress of your web site and frankly I believe the business has more potential than I first envisaged."

"And?"

"If we're going to be working jointly on a vinyl-to-vinyl conversion device, we have common ground anyway." Al paused. "Let's cut to the chase. Now you've dropped the vinyl baggage and changed the name to FindependenceDay.com my partners and I would like to buy a controlling interest in the site. We'd give you a hefty cash settlement and a substantial stake in FEE."

He wrote the figures down on a napkin. Jamie drew a sharp breath. "Do you want the bricks too or just the clicks?"

"We don't want *Platters*," Al said. "If you can make a go of the franchising idea, run with it. We're only interested in the web site. When I was in New York, there was a buzz about Hooray! taking you over. And not just them. My venture capital friends who specialize in dot-coms say there may be other suitors on the horizon. The third wave of the Internet could be the biggest of all."

Jamie's face was inscrutable. A minute passed. Jamie's eyes seemed to be focused on the back of the store. He waited until the last notes of the Elton John song died down, then looked Al directly in the eye. "Naturally, I'll have to get my lawyer and accountant to go over this proposition. And Theo, of course."

"Theo? What's he got to do with this?"

Jamie shrugged. "Just a concerned friend."

Al regarded him quizzically. "Did you tell him about what happened with FEE?"

"I did."

"What does he think?" Al's facial muscles twitched nervously.

"Frankly, he doesn't believe I should have anything to do with you."

"Why are you then?"

"Part of me thinks once bitten, twice shy. Another part tries to practice forgive and forget. We've known each other a long time. And a third part still believes FEE could be my ticket to financial independence."

"That's exactly what it is," Al said.

"Would I have any control, or is this strictly a minority shareholder position?"

"The whole idea is that Hooray! will gain control."

"I know. It's just that this has been my baby."

Al gave him a sympathetic grin. "That's something every business owner must deal with. If you want an exit opportunity and financial freedom, that's the price you pay. So we have a deal?" Al extended his hand.

"Contingent on your board approving the vinyl conversion device and the shares and my guys giving the okay, I believe we might." Jamie shook Al's hand. "Let's cross the t's and dot the i's here same time next week."

Al shook his hand, trying to suppress his growing sense of triumph.

■ ■ ■

Jamie's 50th birthday was just months away. He latched on to the thought of shares in the resurrected Far East Electronica like a condemned man granted pardon. If Hooray! bought the site, the financial payoff could be enormous. Findependence Day was within reach.

But that wasn't the only thing that excited him. Just as important was the chance to leave a legacy. Once he was gone, he knew, the twins would be well provided for. But after the starlit chat with Theo about leaving an enduring legacy for mankind, he was starting to feel good about the vinyl-to-vinyl conversion device. It fit with his call to arms and the "save the music" philosophy that had first won him a global following.

When Jamie updated Sheena on these developments, she was incredulous. "You gave that snake a second chance?" she said on the phone. But she agreed to meet Jamie. They chose an afternoon in early May at the Nineteenth Hole, a café at the golf course adjoining her townhouse.

When the day came, the golfing season had just started. Jamie could see no one but a solitary greens keeper on the course, far off in the distance.

"You need your head read," Sheena said after they'd sat down at their table and ordered drinks.

"Al's not so bad. He was over his head the first time. He was juggling too many balls in the air and there was no one to catch them."

"He betrayed you once. He'll betray you again."

Jamie managed a tense grin and knocked back a third of his beer. He reflected on how down to earth Sheena was and how she complemented his own idealistic tendencies. As she watched a lone foursome putt out on the nearby green, he stole a glance at her face. She was more beautiful than ever. Her emerald green eyes still entranced him, and when she unleashed her 100-megawatt smile—not so often these days—it still had the same electrifying impact on him as it had when he'd courted her so long ago.

Jamie felt his breath speeding up as she looked back and returned his gaze. "What is it?" she said, as if something were wrong.

"Nothing. I was just thinking of when we first started out on this mad trip together."

"It was a grand time." She looked wistfully into the distance, with the faintest hint of a smile forming at the corners of her mouth.

"I really thought that, once we had the twins, we'd go the distance," Jamie said. "'Grow old along with me, the best is yet to be.'" He half sang the lyric from a John Lennon song.

Sheena smiled. "Yes, and for a long time I thought I would be your Yoko Ono."

Jamie extended his hand across the table and lightly clasped hers. "It doesn't have to be like this. I miss you. I don't see nearly enough of Micki and Marco."

Firmly, she returned his hand to his side of the table. "I'm tired of living my life in limbo," she said. "Since you became the big businessman and entrepreneur, you've turned into someone I don't recognize."

"I haven't changed. It's a ton of work trying to build a germ of an idea into a viable business."

She shook her head. "All this talk of becoming a dot-com mogul and a franchising king. It's way bigger than you ever wanted. Whatever happened to the simple guy who sold electronics eight hours a day, then retreated to his study to write beautiful song lyrics half the night?"

"He's still there."

"When was the last time you wrote a song or even sang somebody else's?"

Jamie's face darkened. "You missed my performance at the launch, but that's precisely the point. The whole idea behind Findependence Day was to make it possible for me to do such things whenever I want. And you to write your teen novels. Not when we're old and grey, but while we're still young and vibrant enough to make an impact. Preferably together, two codgers fading off into the sunset together."

Sheena considered this, sipping on her glass of wine. "Surely you can do whatever you want by now."

"Together we might have been able to pull it off. Apart, I have to make a big score from selling the web site."

She looked dubious. "Forget the big score, Jamie. Forget the multi-millionaire dream. Findependence Day is within your grasp without all that. All those years of guerrilla frugality and the lifestyle we lived is what it's all about. It's not about the big score."

He raised his beer to his lips. "Maybe Al will come through after all. Stranger things have happened."

"Maybe."

"If I've learned one thing from him, it's never give up."

"Your web site is being torn apart over this Hooray! deal," Sheena said. "When you approached me about getting some teachers to finance you, there actually was some interest from one of the men on staff."

"You're telling me now?"

"I never pitched him, but it turned out he was a fan and one of your registered users. When I learned that, I told him about the opportunity."

"And?" Jamie tried to suppress the rising tide of excitement welling up in his chest.

"He thought about it for a week. He came back and said he'd been on the site's chat room. He felt there was total anarchy over Hooray! buying you out. It was clear to him that if you sell, a bunch of people will split off from the community and start their own site."

"You talking about Boomerbucks and Nimrod? They'd never do that. They're true-blue Vinylheads. I even gave them administration privileges."

"You're way too trusting. You gave Al another chance. You give people you haven't even met access to your web site."

"Honey, you have to trust somebody. Besides, they promised me they'd never break away to compete with the site."

"You met with them?"

"No, it was in a public discussion on the site. I've never met them in person, although after the launch of *Platters* some of them have been meeting at beer bashes. I imagine that's how this all developed. I know of at least one marriage brought about by the site: Princess and Neanderthal."

Sheena paused as the waiter brought the salad they'd agreed to share. "The point is that's why my teacher friend backed off. I know there's a difference between the web site and the retail operation, but bad vibes in one camp are bound to affect the other. It's not the kind of risk I'd want to expose my colleagues to."

"I hear you. 'Nuff said."

Jamie stole another glance at Sheena, savouring again the perfect shape of her lips. He suppressed the urge to lean over the table and kiss her, right then and there. It had been so long.

"You're going ahead with the sale regardless?" Her face was impassive.

"I don't see what other choice I have."

"In that case…"

Sheena reached for her handbag and retrieved a brown manila envelope. She withdrew it and placed the settlement papers on the table. "All we need to make this official is our signatures and the lawyer's."

"I'm not ready to do that," Jamie's face was ashen. "With all that's happening, I'm just not."

"It's time to get on with our lives."

"Are you still seeing that guy?" Jamie felt a knot constricting his throat.

"I go out occasionally with various friends."

"You know what I mean."

"There's no one special, Jamie. We just need to move on." She stabbed the salad with her fork and ate a mouthful.

"We're still legally married. You're the mother of my children, and I still love you." His pain emerged in his choked voice.

"Jamie, I need closure," she drummed her fingers on the tabletop. "I can't go on with the rest of my life until we deal with this formality. I know your 50th birthday is approaching and how important it is to you, but let me remind you that I'm close to the same milestone myself."

"Formality?" he said indignantly. "We're talking about tearing asunder what God brought together. We're a family. You're part of me. Think about what you're doing. Take some more time."

She did take a second, glancing absent-mindedly at the golf course. Then she fixed him with a gaze, a determined set to her mouth.

"I've thought about it, and this is what I think we should do. Please sign."

"You *think* you should do it?" Jamie saw a ray of hope, "Don't you know it?"

"Who knows anything for sure? There are no certainties, only probabilities. It's highly probable our time together is over."

Her tone was warmer now, and she smiled almost imperceptibly. "We can be friends, of course. We need to be amicable, if only for the sake of Marco and Micki."

"Who said anything about not being amicable? I still love you," Jamie's voice was almost breaking. "That's as plain as I can make it. There's no one else. There never has been."

She looked away again. "I know, Jamie, but it's not about that. It's about too many years of not being here for us. Too much poker. Too much big business. Too much Vegas."

"Sheena, we've been through that," his face was a study of desolation. "I told you what happened."

"You can't undo the law of cause and effect." She looked pointedly at her watch.

"It's a mistake, Sheena. I really believe it." Jamie's face twisted in anguish.

"It may be, who's to say?" Sheena offered him her ballpoint pen.

He grasped it, clicking it in agitation. He glanced at the papers and then looked Sheena directly in the eyes. "This is really what you want?"

She nodded.

"I hope I've made it crystal clear that this is not what I want." The blood had drained from his face.

"I know that."

"And I'd never have forgiven myself if you'd left the door ajar ever so slightly, and I failed to make my best efforts to open it again."

"I acknowledge you tried one last time. Please sign."

"No choice?"

She shook her head, tried a sympathetic smile.

Jamie signed.

■ ■ ■

Two days after the accountants and lawyers signed off on the deal between FEE and FindependenceDay.com, Al reached Jamie at work on his cell phone. He sounded furious. He'd spoken with the president of Hooray! He had informed him that a renegade group within FindependenceDay.com had split off and started their own web site dedicated to financial independence.

The former vinyl community was flocking to join them, he said. "So of course Hooray! has decided not to proceed with the purchase of the site. You bastard," Al said. "You set me up. You knew what was coming down all along."

"I was just as surprised as you are. Believe me. I didn't see their vicious announcement until I signed on yesterday. I'm still reeling from the shock."

"Prove it in court," Al said. "I just got out of a meeting with my partners. They're not happy campers. As the majority owners of FEE, we've decided to sell out your shares at current market value."

"What value?" Jamie said, "You need to have it objectively appraised by a qualified professional to determine that."

"The value is what we say it is. We've put a cheque in the mail for the entire proceeds of the sale of your shares."

"How much is that?"

"$49.37," Al said in an icy tone and hung up.

Chapter 18

Rehearsals for Retirement

[PHIL OCHS, 1969]

J amie stared down at the phone in disbelief. There was an unpleasant constriction in his chest.

As he flipped the phone closed and returned it to his pocket, he looked across the bank of computers in the café and blinked. His vision was blurry. His eyes moistened despite his attempt to stay in control.

He tried to focus on Theo, who was seated across from him.

"Who was that?" Theo said, with a fatherly look of concern.

"Who else? Al."

He recapped the brief conversation.

"Hate to say I told you so."

"I know. What timing."

Jamie gave Theo the details about the trio of former Vinylheads who'd broken away from Jamie's web site to launch their own. "They're competing with us and poaching all our best bloggers and posters," he said.

"Who were the trio?"

"Don't know in real life. Their Internet handles are Boomerbucks, Nimrod and Shankshaft. Always seemed like decent guys. Nimrod's on the west coast. Shankshaft in the east. Not sure where Boomerbucks is. Keeps his cards close to his chest."

"But Hooray! pulled out."

"Only after they learned the community had been split."

"What was their justification for splitting off?"

"They said I'd violated the artistic purity of the Findependence Day community by even considering a sale."

"Opportunists posing as moralists," Theo said, "Did they give you any advance notice?"

"Barely. They informed me yesterday by e-mail one hour before announcing it on the public forums—both mine and their own new one. They'd developed such a following that hundreds of former Vinylheads are following them to the new site. FindependenceDay.com will soon be a ghost of what it used to be."

Theo looked concerned. "They couldn't even pick up the phone? Apparently, loyalty is a dying concept. I wasn't on your site yesterday but the announcement was still up there when I checked in this morning."

Theo paused, a faraway look in his eye. Then he added: "You know, I had an inkling this was going to happen."

"What?" Jamie struggled to focus.

"Through my second identity on the forums I learned a few things from the other participants."

"Like what?" Jamie could barely suppress his curiosity.

"Do you know who Nimrod is in real life?"

"No idea. Some guy who knows a lot about the Internet and investing."

"My sources tell me it's your blogger friend, Nimard."

Jamie gave a start of surprise. "Philippe? You have to be kidding. He's no friend of mine."

"I believe it's the case."

"That would explain a few things." Jamie stroked his chin, deep in thought. "Makes sense."

"There's more," Theo said, almost hesitant to continue.

Jamie's eyes widened, as he nodded for Theo to go on.

"Did you ever meet Boomerbucks in person?"

Jamie's eyes narrowed. "No. Not as far as I'm aware."

Theo smiled. "You've met him alright. He was at the launch of the café."

Jamie cast his mind back to the launch party. There had been a number of Vinyl-heads he'd finally been able to put faces to. But which was Boomerbucks?

He shook his head. "I'm drawing a blank."

Theo looked him in the eye. "Since the group broke away it's become pretty well known on their site who Boomerbucks is," he said.

Jamie was still perplexed. "I can't bear to go on their site. Too painful." Even now, his stomach churned at the thought of the split in the community and the public denunciations of him as the trio tried to justify their action.

Theo gave him a fatherly grin. "Maybe you should go on the site just one time to satisfy your curiosity."

"I can't do that."

"Let me put you out of your misery. You're probably the last to know. Boomerbucks is your friend Al."

Jamie choked on his Coke. He blinked with incredulity. It took a few moments to compose himself. "Boomerbucks is Al?"

Theo nodded.

"But that's impossible. I just talked to Al on the phone. He sounded upset that Nimrod and his cronies had broken away. He was as surprised as I was."

"What can I say? The guy's a great actor. A real Machiavellian character."

Jamie's face was ashen as he tried to figure out what had happened. "So he used the Hooray! overture to justify stealing my web site, then when Hooray! backed off, used the broken deal to justify reneging on my shares in FEE?"

Theo nodded. "That's about the size of it. I wouldn't be surprised if his next move is to reunite the breakaway site with what's left of FindependenceDay.com, then get Hooray! or one of its rivals to buy out the new recombined site."

Jamie shook his head in disbelief. They sat in silence for a few minutes, sipping their Cokes. As the reality of the betrayal began to sink in, Jamie again felt like he'd been punched in the gut.

After about a minute, he said, "Then Al and Nimard knew each other. They probably knew each other before the Vegas fiasco. That bastard! He set me up for the publicity."

Distractedly, he glanced at his cell phone. "And the worst thing is... Know what day this is?"

Theo checked his watch. "Sure, June 15th."

"Two weeks to go till Findependence Day," Jamie said, "and everything collapses. To top it all off, I got a call from one of Didi's producers last week."

"Good old Didi. Been years since I've been on the show."

"You may get another chance. They wanted to know if I'd fly to New York to celebrate my Findependence Day."

"New York? What happened to Chicago?"

"The producer said they wanted to tie it in to the July 4th celebrations in Times Square. Independence Day, don't you know?"

"What did you tell them?"

"I said I could be there, but it might not be a celebration because I'm not sure I've reached my Findependence Day. Then there's Sheena. I told them we're separated, and I don't know if she'd come."

"What did the producer say to that?"

"She said no problem. I should just be there for a July 4th live shoot, and they'd take care of the details. They emailed my ticket yesterday. She was enthusiastic about doing the live show with me. Said they had a big sponsor all lined up."

"I'll bet. Findependence Day has been a godsend to their ratings, not to mention their ad sales."

"I have to admit I don't watch regularly."

"Neither do I," Theo said, "but from the episodes I have caught, it seems Didi has incorporated Findependence Day into her guerrilla frugality shtick. She often uses you as an example of what's possible for these debt-heavy young couples to achieve."

"That's nice, but unfortunately I didn't quite make it. From what I can tell, now that the FEE ownership has come to nothing, I'm at least a year or two away."

"You may be closer than you think." Theo reached into his briefcase and pulled out a spreadsheet of Jamie's finances. He pointed to a graph that had started a sharp ascent five years earlier.

"That's the day the stock market bottomed."

"I remember that," Jamie said. "The leveraged loan. Great timing."

"But I see here you went out a few days after the crash and bought more. Where did you get that money?"

"I didn't borrow more, if that's what you're thinking. I just did what you said and rebalanced. Took some profits on some of my bonds that had capital gains and added to my equity ETF positions. I was pretty nervous about it at the time."

"Good thinking. When interest rates fall the price of bonds rises, an inverse relationship that confuses some new investors. That rebalancing turned out to be a smart move. As you can see from the graph, the stock market's been on a bull run ever since."

"I guess. After that, I stopped paying attention to the daily gyrations of the market. I got caught up in the business. Besides, with the Lazy ETF Portfolio you set up for me, there wasn't much *to* do."

"That's the idea. Busy professionals and businesspeople are better off sticking to their knitting, making money from their core competency. For most of us, picking stocks is not our long suit, to crib a bridge phrase."

"How close was I to making it?"

Theo scrutinized the printout again.

"Let's see. Your Tax Free Savings Accounts have done well because of the market. So has your retirement plan and non-registered investments. Even though Al stiffed you on the FEE shares, it looks like his cheque cleared for the purchase of FindependenceDay.com."

"It did, which means I no longer own it. Now he's cut me out, Al can get rich."

Theo looked pensive. "What profit a man to gain the whole world and lose his soul? Somehow I think he'll meet his karmuppance."

Theo looked back down at the spreadsheet.

"Now as to other streams of income, there's nothing much we can do about the government pensions. You'll just have to wait until your 60s for those."

"Right. Once they kick in, they will slow down the withdrawal rate from the investment portfolio."

Theo pulled out another spreadsheet and scanned it.

"What's that?"

"This is the original plan, the one that had you making it on your 50th birthday."

Jamie looked wistful. "The one where I started the third phase of my life at 50 and Sheena at 55?"

"Right. As you can see, her share of the investment income plus her pension easily puts you over the top."

"Too late," Jamie said.

"Has she signed the agreement too?"

"I assume so. She was going to give me a ding when it was official."

"How are the twins taking it?"

"They're cool. Sheena did a great job raising those two. And I've talked to them straight about everything. They know our separation has nothing to do with them. They've got their own lives, what with college coming up in the fall."

"I see from this that the education savings plans did their job. Even though we slowly moved to bonds the last four years, what was still exposed to the stock market has done very well. But be sure to liquidate the last 25% by August."

"I always do."

"That just about covers it. Any real estate income?"

"Just the REITs and the *Platters* building. Thankfully, Al severed the retail operation from the web site."

"You made sure you retained legal ownership of the building and the business?"

"My lawyer and accountant made sure of it. I still need the rental income from the remaining business tenant and the tenants from the other two apartments."

"Well, I think you've made it, Jamie. All the guerrilla frugality you and Sheena practiced all those years. All the smart investment decisions you made. You don't need Al's big score."

As he listened to Theo's words, Jamie could feel the tight bands loosening from around his chest. But he knew there was nothing that could kill the pain of Al's betrayal.

■ ■ ■

The next day, a well-dressed Japanese businessman walked into the café. His dark rimmed glasses and inscrutable smile were instantly recognizable. It was his old poker nemesis.

"Jimon!" Jamie said, shaking his hand. "Did you come to play poker?"

"I have heard much about your *Platters* games café and wanted to see for myself," Jimon said.

"Let me give you the tour." Proudly, Jamie pointed out the main features of the ground floor, ending the tour in the basement poker salon.

"Let us sit here." Jimon sat on one of the card table chairs. "I wanted you to know that what happened to your web site was not personal. Just business."

Jamie nodded. In spite of himself, his heart started beating faster as the anger and pain returned. "You know about all that?"

Yes," Jimon said. "Riki and I were partners with Mr. Peters and helped him rescue FEE. He shook his head vigorously. "Is not good. Mr. Peters not gentleman."

Jamie pulled out a chair.

"We had, how do you say, major control," Jimon continued.

"Majority ownership."

Jimon nodded. "That's it, majority. When we sell out your shares in FEE at 2 cents a unit, we exercise same right with Mr. Peters' shares."

Jamie stared at him, uncomprehending. "You mean you bought him out for $49.37 too?"

Jimon laughed. "Not exactly. Mr. Peters have many more shares than you. Precise amount of cheque was $7,467 and twenty three cents."

Jamie's eyes widened. "So now he owns neither FEE nor FindependenceDay.com."

Jimon smiled. "So right. Same as you. Riki and I own all."

■ ■ ■

It was 8 pm on July 4th, Jamie's 50th birthday. The red light flashed as the camera came alive, framing the face of Didi Quinlan. She wore a sparkling sequin dress of red, white and blue. A technician brought up the volume of the *Debt March* theme song as the camera zoomed in on Didi's face.

"Hello, viewers across the nation," she burbled with her characteristic enthusiasm. "And welcome to a special edition of *Debt March*, live from New York City!"

The camera panned across the enthusiastic audience, intermixing some live shots from Times Square, where the party was heating up for America's Independence Day. The director cut from a shot of Old Glory waving in the breeze to Didi's patriotically themed dress.

Didi waved her hand to get the audience to quiet down.

"Today we've flown in some old friends who were with us almost since the inception of this show, 25 years ago."

There was a titter of anticipation among the crowd. "It was a close call whether he'd be able to attend tonight, but please welcome Jamie Morelli."

Sustained applause.

"...and..."

Didi waited till she could hear the last two pairs of hands finish clapping, "his financial advisor and great friend of mine, Theodoris Konstantin."

The pair walked on to the raised platform and seated themselves. Jamie and Theo exchanged amused glances about the exaggerated "great friend" comment.

"Jamie," Didi began, leaning forward and looking directly into his eyes, "22 years ago on this very show, you told the world you were hopelessly mired in more than $40,000 of debt. Soon after your first appearance, as our viewers well know, you drew a line in the sand. Just as your marriage vows with Sheena declared your love to the world, you vowed you would be financially independent by the day you turned 50."

The camera zoomed in on Jamie, relaxed and confident in the guest's chair.

"Tell us you made it, Jamie."

Jamie raised his hands and smiled broadly. "So Theo tells me," Jamie said.

The camera moved in on Theo, who was beaming like a proud papa. He nodded. "He made it, alright. Right on the nose. Now that he has, I'm announcing my own full retirement. I'll be 76 next week, and I'm ready." The audience stamped and whistled in approval.

Didi looked at him, genuinely pleased. "Well, all I can say is it's about time, honey." She looked at Jamie.

"Tell me, Jamie. What are you going to do tomorrow? Sleep in? Play golf? Poker, perhaps? Going to be like our newly retired friend, Theo?"

"Apart from flying back home? I hate to disappoint you, Didi, but I'll likely do exactly what I was doing yesterday. I'll be at the *Platters* Internet café, chatting with customers and friends. The more I relax, the harder it is to tell the difference between work and play. I'll be blogging when I feel inspired, writing my columns and running *Platters*."

Didi looked almost disappointed. "No difference at all? So what was the big deal about Findependence Day? It doesn't sound any different than your life before."

"It may seem that way," Jamie said, "but there's one big difference."

"What's that?"

"I don't *have* to do this anymore. If I continue to work, it's because I wish to do it."

"So when I reach my own Findependence Day," Didi said, "I'll just keep on doing this show?"

"We all figure you won't stop till the last advertiser pulls out," Jamie said, drawing laughs. "Many broadcasters like you keep going as long as they can. Look at Larry King or the late Louis Rukeyser. Or Johnny Carson."

"I don't know, honey. If they stop paying me, I'm outta here," Didi wisecracked. "Now, Jamie, the first time you appeared on this show, your wife Sheena was unable to cut up her credit cards."

She leaned down and produced a gleaming pair of scissors. "What would she do if she were asked to do that today?"

Jamie frowned. "I really don't know. You'd have to ask her."

Didi smiled broadly. "Good idea. Why don't we do that?"

A murmur went through the crowd, and a few fingers started pointing at a chair near the front row. One of the cameramen whirled around to frame a shot of a smiling redhead who was now walking up to the set.

Jamie gasped. It was Sheena, more dazzling than ever. As Didi patted the empty seat between her and Jamie, he glanced at Theo, who seemed to be enjoying the proceedings immensely, but didn't look surprised.

Sheena sat down while Didi continued. "Now kiddies, we flew Sheena here to give her a second chance to cut up her credit cards."

Didi made a cutting motion with the scissors and handed them to her new guest. From her handbag, Sheena produced a familiar looking manila envelope. She extracted the marital settlement papers and—using Didi's scissors—cut them up on camera, smiling broadly at Jamie.

Jamie was stricken dumb. Sheena leaned over and kissed him. Didi gave the cameraman a look, and he zoomed in on the happy couple.

"And now the credit card," Didi nagged.

"That's easy." Sheena pulled a credit card from her purse and looked deliberately at the camera. Without hesitation, she cut it in half. The audience roared in approval, with a few wolf whistles piercing through.

"When did you eliminate your credit card debt, Sheena?"

"It must have been six years after the first show," she said. "We became Froogers more than 20 years ago, and one of the first things to go was that awful monster credit card debt."

"I hear that, despite your purchase of a beautiful home after the birth of your twins, you paid off the mortgage in just 13 years?"

"Again, guerrilla frugality worked," Sheena said. "But that's where the story gets complicated."

"I know," Didi said. "I understand you two had split up and sold your dream home. Care to share what happened?"

"The truth is," Sheena began, "we very nearly did split up. I'd strong-armed Jamie into signing the papers just as his business affairs were collapsing. When I first said 'I do' to Jamie, I didn't think I was signing up for life with a business tycoon. The more the web site and *Platters* neared the big time, the more estranged we got."

"What happened?" Didi persisted.

"I kept delaying the moment when I'd actually sign the papers. I heard how his web site deals had fallen apart. Then I talked to Jamie, and he told me one part of him was glad they had. He seemed to feel he'd reconnected with his true self, the self I'd always been in love with."

Didi played to the cameras with a "how sweet" expression.

"If I may," Theo interjected.

Didi looked annoyed, but allowed Theo to continue.

"I'd shown Jamie the numbers. From the get-go I told him—and I remind your viewers—you don't need a big score to achieve financial independence. You need a plan. And you need to adopt a lifestyle that will help you achieve your plan."

The camera panned across the audience, capturing several couples nodding in agreement.

"Jamie doesn't know this," Theo smiled, "but Sheena called me up last week and shared her doubts about proceeding any further with their divorce."

The camera cut to a reaction shot of Didi. For once she was speechless.

"Real estate was always one of their stumbling blocks," Theo continued. "Jamie was never happy about the big home in the suburbs, but it got sold when they split. Now the twins are headed to college in the fall, the townhouse is quite big enough for Sheena and Jamie alone."

Sheena reached for Jamie's hand and placed it in her lap. "Darling, when we fly back home tomorrow night, I'd like you to move into the townhouse with me."

Jamie had just started to recover from the shock. "Guess we'll rent out my apartment above *Platters*. You're going to be a landlord after all."

"Another stream of rental income," Theo beamed. "But that's not all."

Jamie looked puzzled and withdrew his hand from Sheena's.

"When I showed Sheena the numbers, I told her Jamie had been right about the cash flow and profits a second *Platters* location would generate. He didn't need to build a giant corporation with franchises flung around the world. With all the other streams of income we'd built up, all he needed was a little more business income. Sheena called up a teacher friend who had previously expressed interest, and the two of them pooled their funds with a third partner."

Theo gave Didi the thumbs up, and she again took control.

"Now we have a special surprise guest," Didi told the cameras. "Ladies and gentlemen, from Rochester, N.Y., please welcome Victor Morelli, the new manager of America's first *Platters* Internet cafe."

The camera zoomed close on Jamie's surprised face, then pulled out to show his brother strolling on to the set. Victor had always been a taller, older version of Jamie, but now he sported a neatly trimmed beard, grey at the edges. As they embraced, the lights dimmed.

Up from the orchestra came the familiar tune of "Happy Birthday." At Didi's cue, an assistant came on to the set with a birthday cake, 50 candles aglow.

The audience sang along as Didi urged Jamie to blow them out. He succeeded on the fourth try.

"I tried to make the case for guerrilla frugality. I wanted to put only five candles on the cake," Didi smiled. "But I was overruled by my producer."

The *Debt March* credits started to roll. The director switched to a short live feed from Times Square. Superimposed over the clip were the words, "Happy Findependence Day, Jamie."

Epilogue: Grow Old With Me

[JOHN LENNON, 1980]

A week later, Jamie took Sheena for a two-week vacation in Ellicottville, N.Y. A fashionable ski resort in the winter, the charming little village was subdued in the off-season. They walked hand in hand through the main street, ducking in and out of antique shops, used-book stores and real-estate offices.

"Doesn't seem like lakefront properties have come down that much since the housing crunch," Jamie said.

"We can still dream, can't we?" Sheena said. "This is amazing. I can't recall the last time you took two straight weeks off."

"Me neither. Now I know how it feels like to be a teacher and have every summer off."

"A month of Sundays, my father used to say," she smiled, giving him a quick kiss on the cheek.

"Plenty more months like that from now on. Whenever business is slow at *Platters*, I just flip Bernie's old 'Out to Lunch' sign to face the street."

"What if your customers come back an hour later?"

"I had new versions printed up. Right now, the one hanging there says 'Back in two weeks'."

"What?" Sheena stepped back to look at her husband.

"Just kidding, honey. Actually, my staff is great. They keep the place humming when I go fishing."

Sheena put her arm around Jamie to free up more sidewalk for some noisy skateboarders coming up behind them. "All those years you envied my teacher pension, and now you've beaten me to Findependence Day."

"Only because you insist on returning to your beloved teens each fall. What you writers put yourselves through to gather material for your craft."

"I've been thinking about that. For the first time in my life, I'm not aching to return in September."

Jamie stopped and gave her another squeeze. "You know the plan lets you stop now if you want to."

The skateboarders were almost upon them. The sound of the plastic wheels on the pavement was uncomfortably loud. Sheena hugged the curb as they came to a stop. One of the teens turned down his MP3 player and greeted them. A smile came over Jamie's face.

"Guess who, mum?"

Marcello had long since grown taller than his mother, and the skates just amplified the difference. He leant down to embrace her. Michaela did the same with Jamie.

"Is this some kind of a conspiracy?" Sheena said, feigning indignation as she put her hands on her hips.

"It is, mum," Michaela said. "Dad booked us in the adjoining room to your suite at the hotel."

"We'll knock on your door at 5:30, so you can take us to dinner," Marcello said.

"Don't expect a high-end restaurant," Sheena said. "I'm about to become an old age pensioner."

Jamie looked at her, surprised. "Are you saying what I think you're saying?"

Sheena grinned. "That's right. Since I turn 50 this year too, I can take early retirement. The pension will be reduced a bit, so from now on, we'll have to watch our pennies."

"It's okay, mum, our treat," Marcello said. "If you're celebrating your own Findependence Day we're taking you to the Silver Fox."

Sheena looked puzzled.

Michaela explained. "You know the lump sum of money we got from grandma's inheritance?"

Sheena nodded.

"I'm sure you know the stock market has been booming the last two years," Michaela said. "The part of our education plans and trust fund that was invested in the market has done very well."

Michaela resumed skating, her brother two steps behind. Marcello looked back and yelled, "5:30. Cocktails and sodas on the terrace."

A Peek into Theo's Library

Good Debt, Bad Debt, Jon Hanson, Penguin, 2005.

The Millionaire Next Door: The Surprising Secrets of America's Wealthy, Thomas Stanley and William Danko, Longstreet Press, 1996.

Beyond Work: How Accomplished People Retire Successfully, Bill Roiter, Wiley, 2008.

The New Retirement: How It Will Change Our Future, Sherry Cooper, Penguin Canada, 2007.

How I Stopped Worrying About Retirement (Without Alcohol, Nicotine, Caffeine or Other Artificial Stimulants), Bruce McDougall, Prentice Hall Canada Inc., 2001.

How to Retire Happy Wild and Free. Ernie Zelinksi, Ten Speed Press, 2004.

The Retirement Time Bomb, Gordon Pape, Penguin Canada, 2005.

How Much Is Enough? Balancing Today's Needs with Tomorrow's Retirement Goals, Diane McCurdy, McGraw-Hill Ryerson, 2001.

The Number: A Completely Different Way to Think About the Rest of Your Life, Lee Eisenberg, Simon & Schuster, 2006.

Conserving Client Portfolios During Retirement, William Bengen, FPA Press, 2006.

Are You a Stock or a Bond? Create Your Own Pension Plan for a Secure Financial Future, Moshe Milevsky, FT Press, 2008.

Mathematics: Making Financial Decisions 11, McGraw-Hill Ryerson, 2001.

Stocks for the Long Run, Jeremy Siegel, McGraw Hill, 2002 (4th ed).

Multiple Streams of Income: How to Generate a Lifetime of Unlimited Wealth, Robert Allen, Wiley & Sons, 2005.

Your Money or Your Life: Transforming Your Relationship with Money and Achieving Financial Independence, Joe Dominguez and Vicki Robin, Penguin, 1999.

Stumbling on Happiness, Daniel Gilbert, Vintage Canada, 2007.

Am I Going to be OK? Achieving Financial Comfort in Today's World, Francis D'Andrade, Per Capita Publishing, 2006.

Your Money & Your Brain: How the New Science of Neuroeconomics Can Help Make You Rich, Jason Zweig, Simon & Schuster, 2007.

The Wisdom of Insecurity, Alan Watts, Vintage ed, 1968.

The Wealthy Barber: The Common Sense Guide to Successful Financial Planning, David Chilton, Stoddart, 1989.

The Richest Man in Babylon, George S. Clason, Signet, 2004.

The Automatic Millionaire: A Powerful One-Step Plan to Live and Finish Rich, David Bach, Broadway Books, 2003.

Financial Freedom Without Sacrifice, Talbot Stevens, Financial Success Strategies, 1993.

The Cottage, the Spider Brooch and the Second Wife: How to Overcome the Challenges of Estate Planning, Sandy Cardy, ECW Press, 2004.

The Family Fight: Planning to Avoid It, Barry Fish and Les Kotzer, Continental Atlantic Publications Inc., 2008.

The Four Pillars of Investing: Lessons for Building a Winning Portfolio, William Bernstein, McGraw Hill, 2002.

Unconventional Success: A Fundamental Approach to Personal Investment, David Swensen, Simon & Schuster, 2005.

The Empowered Investor: A Guide to Building Better Portfolios, Keith Matthews (2nd edition); Book Coach Press, 2008.

What Wall Street Doesn't Want You to Know: How You Can Build Real Wealth Investing in Index Funds, Larry Swedroe, St. Martin's Press, 2004.

Common Sense on Mutual Funds: New Imperatives for the Intelligent Investor, John Bogle, John Wiley & Sons, 1999.

The New Investment Frontier III, Howard Atkinson with Donna Green, Insomniac Press, 2005.

Index Funds: The 12-Step Program for Active Investors, Mark Hebner, Index Funds Advisors Inc., 2007.

The Intelligent Investor, Benjamin Graham, 2003 Collins edition updated by Jason Zweig.

Asset Dedication: How to Grow Wealthy with the Next Generation of Asset Allocation, Stephen J. Huxley & J. Brent Burns, McGraw Hill Professional, 2004.

No Hype: The Straight Goods on Investing, Gail Bebee, The Ganneth Company, 2008.

ABOUT THE AUTHOR

Jonathan Chevreau has been the personal finance columnist for the Financial Post since 1996 and for the National Post since its launch in 1998. He lives in Long Branch, Ontario.

He has previously authored or co-authored seven non-fiction financial books. They include the *Smart Funds* series and *The Wealthy Boomer: Life After Mutual Funds* (Key Porter Books); and *Krash!* (McGraw Hill.)

He blogs at www.wealthyboomer.ca.

Findependence Day is his second novel. For more information, see www.findependenceday.com.